Malayan Literature

COMPRISING
ROMANTIC TALES, EPIC POETRY
AND
ROYAL CHRONICLES

TRANSLATED INTO ENGLISH FOR THE FIRST TIME

WITH A SPECIAL INTRODUCTION BY
CHAUNCEY C. STARKWEATHER, A.B., LL.B.

REVISED EDITION

D0124118

COPYRIGHT, 1901
BY THE COLONIAL PRESS

SPECIAL INTRODUCTION

EASILY the most charming poem of Malayan Literature is the Epic of Bidasari. It has all the absorbing fascination of a fairy tale. We are led into the dreamy atmosphere of haunted palace and beauteous plaisance: we glide in the picturesque imaginings of the oriental poet from the charm of all that is languorously seductive in nature into the shadowy realms of the supernatural. At one moment the sturdy bowman or lithe and agile lancer is before us in hurrying column, and at another we are told of mystic sentinels from another world, of Djinns and demons and spirit-princes. All seems shadowy, vague, mysterious, entrancing.

In this tale there is a wealth of imagery, a luxury of picturesqueness, together with that straightforward simplicity so alluring in the story-teller. Not only is our attention so captivated that we seem under a spell, but our sympathy is invoked and retained. We actually wince before the cruel blows of the wicked queen. And the hot tears of Bidasari move us to living pity. In the poetic justice that punishes the queen and rewards the heroine we take a childish delight. In other words, the oriental poet is simple, sensuous, passionate, thus achieving Milton's ideal of poetic excellence. We hope that no philosopher, philologist, or ethnologist will persist in demonstrating the sun-myth or any other allegory from this beautiful poem. It is a story, a charming tale, to while away an idle hour, and nothing more. All lovers of the simple, the beautiful, the picturesque should say to such learned peepers and botanizers, "Hands off!" Let no learned theories rule here. Leave this beautiful tale for artists and lovers of the story pure and simple. Seek no more moral here than you would in a rose or a lily or a graceful palm. Light, love, color, beauty, sympathy, engaging fascination—these may be found alike by philosopher and winsome youth. The story is no more immoral than a drop of dew or a lotus bloom; and, as to interest, in the land of the improviser and the story-teller one is obliged to be interesting. For there the audience is either spellbound, or quickly fades away and leaves the poet to realize that he must attempt better things.

We think that these folk-stories have, indeed, a common origin, but that it is in the human heart. We do not look for a Sigurd or Siegfried on every page. Imagine a nation springing from an ignorant couple on a sea-girt isle, in a few generations they would have evolved their Sleeping Beauty and their Prince Charming, their enchanted castles, and their Djinns and fairies. These are as indigenous to the human heart as the cradle-song or the battle-cry. We do not find ourselves siding with those who would trace everything to a first exemplar. Children have played, and men have loved, and poets have sung from the beginning, and we need not run to Asia for the source of everything. Universal human nature has a certain spontaneity.

The translator has tried to reproduce the faithfulness and, in some measure, to indicate the graceful phrases of the original poem. The author of Bidasari is unknown, and the date of the poem is a matter of the utmost uncertainty. Some have attributed to it a Javanese origin, but upon very slight evidence. The best authorities place its scene in the country of Palembang, and its time after the arrival of the Europeans in the Indian archipelago, but suggest that the legend must be much older than the poem.

The "Makota Radja-Radja" is one of the most remarkable books of oriental literature. According to M. Aristide Marre, who translated it into French, its date is 1603. Its author was Bokhari, and he lived at Djohore. It contains extracts from more than fifty Arab and Persian authors. It treats of the duties of man to God, to himself and to society, and of the obligations of sovereigns, subjects, ministers, and officers. Examples are taken from the lives of kings in Asia. The author has not the worst opinion of his work, saying distinctly that it is a complete guide to happiness in this world and the next. He is particularly copious in his warnings to copyists and translators, cautioning them against the slightest negligence or inaccuracy, and promising them for faithfulness a passport to the glories of heaven. This shows that the author at least took the work seriously. That there is not a trace of humor in the book would doubtless recommend it to the dignified and lethargic orientals for whom it was written. Bokhari seemed to consider himself prophet, priest, and poet-laureate in one. The work has a high position in the Malayan Peninsula, where it is read by young and old. The " Crown of Kings " is written in the court language of Djohore. The author was a Mohammedan mendicant monk. He called the book the Crown of Kings because " every king who read and followed its precepts would be a perfect king, and thus only would his crown sit well on his head, and the book itself will be for him a true crown."

La Fontaine and Lamartine loved stories. The schoolmates of the latter called the latter " story-lover." They would have loved the story of the Princess Djouher Manikam, which is written in a simple and natural style and is celebrated in the East, or, as the Malays say, in the " country between windward and leeward."

From the " Sedjaret Malayou," worthless as it is as history, one may obtain side lights upon oriental life. Manners are portrayed in vivid colors, so that one may come to have a very accurate knowledge of them. Customs are depicted from which one may learn of the formality and regard for precedents which is a perspicuous trait of oriental character. The rigid etiquette of court and home may be remarked. From the view of morals here described, one may appreciate how far we have progressed in ethical culture from that prevailing in former times among the children of these winterless lands.

The readers of this series are to be congratulated in that they are here placed in possession of a unique and invaluable source of information concerning the life and literature of the far-away people of the Indian archipelago. To these pages an added interest accrues from the fact that the Philippines are now protected by our flag.

The name Malay signifies a wanderer. As a people they are passionate, vain, susceptible, and endowed with a reckless bravery and contempt of death. The Malays have considerable originality in versification. The pantoum is particularly theirs

—a form arising from their habits of improvisation and competitive versifying. They have also the epic or *sjair*, generally a pure romance, with much naïve simplicity and natural feeling. And finally, they have the popular song, enigma, and fable.

And so we leave the reader to his pleasant journey to the lands of Djinns and Mantris and spells and mystic talismans. He will be entertained by the chrestomathy of Bokhari; he will be entranced by the story of the winsome and dainty Bidasari.

Chauncey C. Starkweather

CONTENTS

THE EPIC OF BIDASARI

—

[*Metrical Translation by Chauncey C. Starkweather, A.B., LL.B.*]

BIDASARI

SONG I

HEAR now the song I sing about a king
　　Of Kembajat. A fakir has completed
　　The story, that a poem he may make.
There was a king, a sultan, and he was
Handsome and wise and perfect in all ways,
Proud scion of a race of mighty kings.
He filled the land with merchants bringing wealth
And travellers. And from that day's report,
He was a prince most valorous and strong,
Who never vexing obstacles had met.
But ever is the morrow all unknown.
After the Sultan, all accomplished man,
Had married been a year, or little more,
He saw that very soon he'd have an heir.
At this his heart rejoiced, and he was glad
As though a mine of diamonds were his.
Some days the joy continued without clouds.
But soon there came the moment when the prince
Knew sorrow's blighting force, and had to yield
His country's capital. A savage bird,
Garouda called, a very frightful bird,
Soared in the air, and ravaged all the land.
It flew with wings and talons wide outstretched,
With cries to terrify the stoutest heart.
All people, great and small, were seized with dread.
And all the country feared and was oppressed,
And people ran now this way and now that.
The folk approached the King. He heard the noise
As of a fray, and, angry, asked the guard,
" Whence comes this noise? " As soon as this he said

One of his body-guard replied with awe,
" Illustrious lord, most merciful of kings,
A fell garouda follows us about."
The King's face paled when these dread words he heard.
The officers arose and beat their breasts.
The sorrow of the King was greater still
Because the Queen was ill. He took her hand
And started without food or anything.
He trusted all to God, who watches o'er
The safety of the world. The suff'ring Queen
Spoke not a word and walked along in tears.
They went by far *campongs* and dreary fields
Beneath a burning sun which overwhelmed
Their strength. And so the lovely Queen's fair face
From palest yellow grew quite black. The prince
Approached the desert with his body torn
By thorns and brambles. All his care and grief
Were doubled when he saw his lovely wife
Who scarce could drag herself along and whom
He had to lead. Most desolate was he,
Turning his mind on the good Queen's sad lot.
Upon the way he gave up all to her.
Two months they journeyed and one day they came
Unto a *campong* of a merchant, where
They looked for rest because the Queen was weak.
The path was rugged and the way was hard.
The prince made halt before the palisades,
For God had made him stop and rest awhile.
The Sultan said: " What is this *campong* here?
I fain would enter, but I do not dare."
The good Queen wept and said: " O my beloved,
What shall I say? I am so tired and weak
I cannot journey more." The King was quite
Beside himself and fainted where he sat.
But on they journeyed to the riverside,
Stopping at every step.
                    And when the King
Had gained the bank he saw a little boat
With roof of bent bamboos and *kadjang* screen.
Then to the Queen, " Rest here, my precious one."

The silver moon was at the full, but veiled
With clouds, like to a maid who hides her face
And glances toward her lover timidly.
Then there was born a daughter, like a flower,
More beautiful than statue of pure gold,
Just like the tulips that the princess plucked.
The mother's heart was broken at the thought
That she must leave the babe, the child beloved
They both adored, such beauty it presaged.
The King with tears exclaimed, " How can we take
The infant with us o'er this stony road
Beset with thorns, and burned with dreadful heat?
Pearl of my palace, said he to the Queen,
" Weep not so bitterly about the child.
An offering let us make of her to God.
God grant she may be found by loving hearts
Who'll care for her and raise her in their home."
As soon as they had quite determined there
To leave the infant princess, their great grief
No limit knew. But ere they went away
The King took up the infant in his arms
And rocked her on his knees until she slept.
" Sleep on, heart's love, my soul, my little one,
Weep not for thy dear mother's lot. She fain
Would take thee with her, but the way is hard.
Sleep on, dear child, the apple of my eye,
The image of thy sire. Stay here, fear not.
For unto God we trust thee, Lord of all.
Sleep on, my child, chief jewel of my crown,
And let thy father go. To look at thee
Doth pierce my heart as by a poniard's blow.
Ah, sweet my child, dear, tender little one,
Thy father loves yet leaves thee. Happy be,
And may no harm come nigh thee. Fare thee well."
The little princess slept, lulled by his voice.
He put her from his knees and placed her on
A finely woven cloth of Ind, and covered her
With satin webbed with gold. With flowing tears
The mother wrapped her in a tissue fine
Adorned with jewels like to sculptured flowers.

She seized the child and weeping murmured **low:**
" O dearest child, my pretty little girl!
I leave thee to the Master of the world.
Live happily, although thy mother goes
And leaves thee here. Ah, sad thy mother's **lot!**
Thy father forces her to quit thee now.
She would prefer with thee to stay, but, no!
Thy father bids her go. And that is why
Thy mother's fond heart breaks, she loves thee so,
And yet must leave thee. Oh, how can I live?"
The mother fainted, and the grieving King
Was fain to kill himself, so was he moved.
He took the Queen's head on his knees. And **soon**
By God's decree and ever-sheltering grace
She to her senses came and stood erect.
Again she wept on looking at the child.
" If I should never see thee more, sweet soul,
Oh, may thy mother share thy fate! Her life
Is bound to thine. The light is gone from out
Thy mother's eyes. Hope dies within her heart
Because she fears to see thee nevermore.
Oh, may some charitable heart, my child,
Discover thee!" The prince essayed **to dry**
Her tears. "Now come away, my dearest love.
Soon day will dawn." The prince in grief set **out,**
But ever turned and wanted to go back.
They walked along together, man and wife
All solitary, with no friends at hand,
Care-worn and troubled, and the moon shone bright.

SONG II

I SING in this song of a merchant great
 And of his wealth. His goods and treasures were
 Beyond all count, his happiness without
Alloy. In Indrapura town there was
No equal to his fortune. He possessed
A thousand slaves, both old and young, who came
From Java and from other lands. His rank
Was higher than Panggawa's. Wives he had
In goodly numbers. But he lacked one thing
That weighed upon his heart—he had no child.
Now, by the will of God, the merchant great
Came very early from the palace gates,
And sought the river-bank, attended by
His favorite wife. Lila Djouhara was
The merchant's name. He heard a feeble voice
As of an infant crying, like the shrill
Tones of a flute, and from a boat it seemed
To come. Then toward the wondrous boat he went
And saw an infant with a pretty face.
His heart was overjoyed as if he had
A mine of diamonds found. The spouses said:
" Whose child is this? It surely must belong
To one of highest rank. Some cause he had
To leave her here." The merchant's heart was glad
To see the bright eyes of the little one.
He raised her in his arms and took her home.
Four waiting-maids and nurses two he gave
The pretty child. The palace rooms were all
Adorned anew, with rugs and curtains soft,
And tapestries of orange hue were hung.
The princess rested on a couch inlaid with gold,
A splendid couch, with lanterns softly bright
And tapers burning with a gentle ray.

The merchant and his wife with all their hearts
Adored the child, as if it were their own.
She looked like Mindoudari, and received
The name of Bidasari.   Then they took
A little fish and changing vital spirits
They put it in a golden box, then placed
The box within a casket rich and rare.
The merchant made a garden, with all sorts
Of vases filled with flowers, and bowers of green
And trellised vines.   A little pond made glad
The eyes, with the precious stones and topaz set
Alternately, in fashion of the land
Of Pellanggam, a charm for all.   The sand
Was purest gold, with alabaster fine
All mixed with red pearls and with sapphires blue.
And in the water deep and clear they kept
The casket.   Since they had the infant found,
Sweet Bidasari, all the house was filled
With joy.   The merchant and his wife did naught
But feast and clap their hands and dance.   They watched
The infant night and day.   They gave to her
Garments of gold, with necklaces and gems,
With rings and girdles, and quaint boxes, too,
Of perfume rare, and crescent pins and flowers
Of gold to nestle in the hair, and shoes
Embroidered in the fashion of Sourat.
By day and night the merchant guarded her.
So while sweet Bidasari grew, her lovely face
Increased in beauty.   Her soft skin was white
And yellow, and she was most beautiful.
Her ear-rings and her bracelets made her look
Like some rare gem imprisoned in a glass.
Her beauty had no equal, and her face
Was like a nymph's celestial.   She had gowns
As many as she wished, as many as
A princess fair of Java.   There was not
A second Bidasari in the land.

I'll tell about Djouhan Mengindra now,
Sultan of Indrapura.   Very wide

His kingdom was, with ministers of state
And officers, and regiments of picked
Young warriors, the bulwark of the throne.
This most illustrious prince had only been
Two years the husband of fair Lila Sari,
A princess lovable and kind. The King
Was deemed most handsome. And there was within
All Indrapura none to equal him.
His education was what it should be,
His conversation very affable.
He loved the princess Lila Sari well.
He gave her everything, and she in turn
Was good to him, but yet she was so vain.
"There is no one so beautiful as I,"
She said. They were united like unto
The soul and body. And the good King thought
There could not be another like his wife.
One day they were together, and the Queen
Began to sing: "Oh, come, my well-beloved,
And listen to my words. Thou tellst me oft
Thou lovest me. But I know not thy heart.
If some misfortune were to overwhelm
Wouldst thou be true to me?" He smiled and said:
"No harm can touch thee, dear. But should it come,
Whenever thou art 'whelmed I'll perish too."
With joy the princess said: "My noble prince,
If there were found a woman whose flower face
Were fairer than all others in the world,
Say, wouldst thou wed her?" And the King replied:
"My friend, my fairest, who is like to thee?
My soul, my princess, of a noble race,
Thou'rt sweet and wise and good and beautiful.
Thou'rt welded to my heart. No thought of mine
Is separate from thee."

     The princess smiled;
Her face was all transfigured with her joy.
But suddenly the thought came to her mind,
"Who knows there is none more fair than I?"
And then she cried: "Now hear me, O my love!
Were there a woman with an angel-face,

Vol. 49—15

Wouldst thou make her thy wife? If she appeared
Unto thine eyes more beautiful than I,
Then would thy heart not burn for her?"

                             The prince
But smiled, and answered not. She also smiled,
But said, " Since thou dost hesitate, I know
That thou wouldst surely wed her." Then the prince
Made answer: " O my heart, gold of my soul,
If she in form and birth were like to thee
I'd join her with thy destiny." Now when
The princess heard these words she paled and shook.
With eyes cast down, she left her royal spouse.
But quick he seized her. With a smile he said:
" Gold, ruby, dearest friend, I pray thee now,
Oh, be not vexed with me. Light of my eyes,
Keep not within thy heart a bitterness
Because I answered thus unto thy words."
He took her in his arms and kissed her lips
And wooed her. And her face again grew sweet
The while she heard. And yet her woman's heart
Was grieved and saddened. And she sat apart,
And swift these thoughts came to her anxious mind:
" I'll seek to-morrow through this kingdom wide,
Lest there should be within the land a maid
More fair than I. To death I shall condemn
Her straight, lest rival she may be to me.
For if my lord should marry her, he'd love
Her more than me. He'd love the younger one,
And constantly my tortured heart would bleed."
They angered her, these thoughts, as if her heart
Were filled with gall. " Now may I be accursed
If I go not unto the end in love."
Her heart was not assuaged; she sighed alone.
Upon the morrow morn the King went out,
And with him many officers and men.
Meanwhile the Princess Lila Sari sent
A summons to a jeweller of skill,
And at the same time called her four *dyangs*,
Who came and sat. Dang Wilapat bowed low
And said, " Our greetings to thee, princess great."

The Queen replied: " Go forth, *dyangs*, at once
And find me gold and dust of gold, and take
It all unto a goldsmith. Let him make
For me a fan, all decked with beauteous gems,
With rubies red and pearls; and after that
A girdle virginal. Count not the price.
I want it all as quickly as may be."
And so they hastened, took the gold, and went
Outside the city, through the whole *campong*
Of goldsmiths, seeking there the best to make
The fan and girdle. And the hammered gold
Soon shone with many amethysts and gems.
It was a marvel to behold those rare
And quaintly fashioned ornaments, to deck
A sultaness. Of priceless worth they were.
Four days, and all was ready for the Queen.
But she had never eaten all this time
Because of grief. She thought the fan more fine
Than Java princess ever yet possessed.
She called the four *dyangs* and said to them:
" A secret mission have I now for ye.
Go up and down among the officers
And show this fan for sale, but never name
The price. Seek ever if there be a face
More beautiful than mine; and should ye find
A face more fair, come tell it straight to me.
If ye obey my will I'll make ye all
Inspectresses within the royal home."
Then forth the women went upon the quest.
And first among their friends they went with words
Of mystery and hints of wondrous things
They had for sale. And so these servants bore
The story to their masters, " The *dyangs*
Have something wonderful to sell." And soon
The daughters of the houses rich began
To clamor for a sight of this great prize.
Then the *dyangs* went to the houses all.
The young girls said, " Oh, tell us now the price."
Dyang Wiravan quickly answered, then
Dyang Podagah: " 'Tis a princely thing;

I'll go and ask the price and tell it thee."
And so they spoke, and so they looked about
To find a face more beautiful and rare
Than their own Queen's, and wearied in the search.
" Where can we further look? " they said, and then
Bethought them of the strangers and the priests.
But in that quarter no one dared to touch
The precious things, but thought it passing strange
The Queen should wish to sell. To the *campong*
Of merchants next they went. A double line
Of ramparts guarded it. " Here is more stir
And gayety," they said, " with sport and song,
Than elsewhere have we found." And so they sought
The richest merchants. " We have something rare,"
They said, " made by an artist Javanese."
When Bidasari's servants saw these folk
They said: " Bring these things to our house and we
Will show them to our master. He will buy."
Then the *dyangs* with smiles replied: " They are
Not ours, but our good Queen's. And only we
May show them, lest a stone be lost, perchance,
And we be punished." Bidasari's maids
Were glad and said, " Wait but a moment here
Until we find what Bidasari wills."
They found her with her maids, and told the tale.
Then Bidasari bade them bring to her
The stranger folk, and said, " If I be pleased
I'll buy." Dang Ratna Watie went and told
The women that young Bidasari wished
To see their wares. The four *dyangs* came in
Together. Joy their faces all suffused,
But they seemed timid, modest, full of fear.
Then Bidasari's women said to them:
" Come, O young women, all are loyal here.
Enter, our sisters and our friends."
                                        Now when
The Queen's *dyangs* had looked about them there
They all were dazzled, Bidasari's face
So beautiful appeared. How beat their hearts!
As they upon her lovely features gazed,

Each murmured to herself, " She is more fair
Than our great Queen."
                     Then Bidasari wished
To buy the fan, and sent a maid to ask
Her parents for the gold. The merchant said,
" Go see what thing it is, and weigh the gold
For her." The mother feared a trap or trick.
" Oh, do not buy the fan, my child," she said;
" I'll buy a finer one for thee. Send this
Away." But when her father saw her tears
Of disappointment, " It is thine," he said.
" What is the price? I'd buy it though it cost
Thy weight in gold, my darling. Tell me now,
Dyangs." Tjendra Melinee answered him,
" Are two timbangs too much? " " I'm very poor,"
He said; " but I will buy it for the child."
The gold was weighed. The four *dyangs* straightway
Departed, hurried to the Queen and said:
" At last we have discovered, O our Queen,
What thou hast sought. 'Tis in a near *campong*
Of merchants very rich and great. Oh, there
We found a princess fairer than the day;
More like an angel than a mortal maid.
No woman in this land compares with her.
Her name is Bidasari. And the King
Would surely marry her if once they met,
For soon she will be ready for a spouse;
Her innocence is charming. Like a cloud
The merchant and his wife keep watchful guard.
Her hair is curly, like a flower full blown.
Her brow is like the moon but one day old.
She's like a ring in Peylou made. She would
Outshine thy beauty, shouldst thou bring her here."
The princess heard and quickly said: " I feel
My hatred rise. Oh, may I never see
Her face! To hear ye speak of her inflames
My heart with anger. Say, why do ye think
That she's more fair than I? " Then made reply
The women: " Bidasari's eyes are soft.
Her smile is sweet, her skin is tinted like

The green *tjempakka*, and her graceful form
Resembles some famed statue nobly made.
Her cheeks are like the bill of flying bird.
We loved to look upon her neck. Her nose
Is like a jasmine bud. Her pretty face
Is like the yellow of an egg. Her thoughts
Are pure as crystal. And she wears her hair
In such a charming way. Her lips are like
A little polished box. The flowers she wears
But make her look the prettier. Her teeth
Are like a bright pomegranate. Ah, the heart
Doth open when one looketh on her face.
She's like a princess of the Mount Lidang.
Her features are like those of Nilagendi.
Her heels are like the eggs of hens, and make
Her seem a princess of Siam. Her fingers
More tapering are than quills of porcupine.
And solid is the nail of her left hand.
No noble's girl is Bidasari's peer."
Now when the princess heard them sing her praise
Her soul was wounded as if by a thorn.
Her dark eyes flashed. "Ah, speak no more of her,"
She said, "nor speak abroad what ye have seen.
But bring me Bidasari. I would see
If what ye say be true."
                              "Then we must take
Her presents first, and strive to gain by them
Her friendship, and attain our end at last."
They went to see her every day, and bore
Rich gifts.
                    The merchant and his wife remarked
The visits of the Queen's *dyangs*, and how
They loved their daughter. That is why they gave
Them all that they desired. But the *dyangs*
Among themselves kept saying: "How can we
Take her away? We love her so, and deep
Within our hearts we pity her. And now
Her parents have such trust in us, and load
Us down with gifts. But when, alas, at home
The princess questions us, what shall we say?

For she's a powerful Queen. Yet if we make
Unhappy this dear girl of these good folk,
Shall we not sin? And still the princess is
So violent and harsh! Her jealousy
Would know no limit should the King but hear
Of this affair."
                              Dang Djoudah answering spoke:
" We all can go to her and quiet her.
A word suffices oft. She is our Queen,
But to the King belongeth power supreme.
If Bidasari should disdain the throne
We shall renounce our functions at the court,
For what the Queen desires is most unjust.
And if we prove unfaithful we shall be
O'erwhelmed with maledictions." Thus they spoke
And went back to the busy-lived *campong*
Of merchants. Here they thought to go and find
Djouhara, and obtain what they desired.
A messenger went after them and said:
" To Dang Bidouri: Come at once; my friend
The princess summons you." Then the *dyangs*
Went to the Queen and found her with the King
At dinner. With malicious wink of eye
She made them understand they must not talk
Before the prince. When he had dined he took
Some *siri* from the betel-box, himself
Anointed with a perfume sweet, and went
To teach the young folk how to ride and shoot
The arrow straight, and played at many games.
Meanwhile the princess Lila Sari called
Before her the *dyangs* and questioned them:
" Why have ye come so late? " Bidouri bowed
And said: " 'Twas very hard to bring her here
To thee. The merchant and his wife do not
A moment leave her, for they love her so.
Her tiring-women ever are about.
Thou shouldst demand her of her parents, if
Thou dost desire to see her. Treat her like
Thy child, for she is still so very young!
From Bidasari's father thou wilt gain

All that thou canst desire, he is so rich,
If thou wilt only love his daughter dear.
And dost thou give command to bring her here?
Let us go all alone and summon her
For Bidasari 'll freely follow us."
They tried to calm the anger of the Queen.
She bowed her head in silence, but her soul
Was very heavy, and hypocrisy
With hate and envy vied within her heart.
" They love the child, these *dyangs*," to herself
She said, " and I shall have no easy task.
I shall attract her here by trickery,
But she shall never my companion be.
With Bidasari once within my power
My heart will be no longer on the rack.
Go now, *dyangs*," she said, " and seek for me
The merchant and his wife and hither bring
Young Bidasari, whom I'll elevate
Unto the rank of princess, for I have
No child. Mazendra take with ye. And when
Young Bidasari shall arrive, conceal
Her for a day or two. And gently speak
Unto the merchant and his wife, and say
Concessions will be granted to the priests
And strangers in their quarter, should she come.
Console Lila Djouhara thus, and pledge
That he may come to see his child whene'er
His heart impelleth him." An escort went
With them, and the *dyangs* bowed low before
The merchant and his wife, and greeted, too,
Fair Bidasari. But the merchant said:
" Why come ye here in so great numbers? " Then
They straight replied: " Our most belovèd Queen
Hath sent us here with greetings unto thee,
The master of the house. If thou'lt permit,
We've come to seek fair Bidasari here."
They beat their breasts, the merchant and his wife.
" Our darling, only child! It will be hard
For her to be the servant of a prince;
For she hath had her way so long! Her traits

Are not yet formed.   Go back, *dyangs*, and pray
The Queen to pardon us.   Say how we grieve."
But the *dyangs* repeated all the words
Said by the Queen, and so their fears were calmed.
They hoped Queen Lila Sari would love well
Fair Bidasari.   Then the merchant said:
" I will obey, and let my darling go,
So that she may become unto the Queen
A servant, and perchance a daughter loved.
Now shall she go with ye.   Only I beg
The Queen to let her come back home to us
At three days' end.   She is not used to stay
With strangers.   Never hath she left us for
A single day."   Then Dang Bidouri said:
" We'll do our best before the Queen ; and why
Should she not grant to Bidasari this ? "
They bathed fair Bidasari with sweet scents,
And then arranged her in rich raiment new.
A fine *sijrash* she wore with broidered flowers
Of Pekan, and a satin robe all fringed
With gold.   She bore a plaque of beaten gold
Bound to a necklace, chiselled, gem-bedecked ;
Her over-tunic was of yellow silk
With tiny serpents on the buttons 'graved.
Three bracelets wore the maid, and rarest rings,
And ear-rings like a wheel in motion wrought.
Chaste links of gold set forth her beauty rare,
A fair flow'r in a vase, whose perfume sweet
Wafts scented breaths as far as one may see.
They kissed her then with tears and held her close
Upon their breasts.   " Be humble to the Queen,"
They said, " remember that thou art before
The King, and near the throne.   Ask leave to come
To see us when thou dost desire.   Speak sweetly
With low and gentle voice."

                                        Thus they enjoined.
And then the merchant said, " *Dyangs*, if ye
Love Bidasari, see ye vex her not."
They dried their tears and said : " Be without fear.
Intrust thy daughter to our mistress dear."

"My child," he said, "I'll come to see thee oft.
Thou wilt be better there, my love, than here."
But Bidasari wept and cried: "Oh, come,
Dear mother, with me! Wilt thou not, alas?"
But the fond parents were astounded then
To learn the mother was not asked to come.
She stayed with tears, the while the father went.
As far as to the city's gates. With tears
He said: "Farewell, O apple of my eye
I leave thee here. Fear not, my dearest child."
Then Bidasari wept. Her heart was wrung.
She went. The merchant followed with his eyes.
She entered by a hidden door. *Dyangs*
And *mandars* flocked to see her, but she hung
Her head and kept her eyes downcast.

                                    The sun
Announced the evening, and the King was still
Surrounded by his officers. 'Twas then
Fair Bidasari to the palace came,
And stood before the Queen. All the *dyangs*
Sat on the floor, with servants of the house.
Like the *pengawas* Bidasari bowed,
'Mid the *dyangs*, in presence of the Queen.
They gave her all the merchant's gifts, as sign
Of homage. All astonished was the Queen
At Bidasari's beauty. She appeared
Almost divine. Bidouri spoke and said,
"Thou seest Bidasari, O our Queen,
Lila Djouhari's daughter." At these words
The Queen was stupefied, and thought: "In truth
'Tis as they said. She is more lovely than
The fairest work of art." Bidouri told
All that the merchant and his wife had said.
The Queen inclined her head and silence kept,
But wicked thoughts were surging in her brain.
A combat raged within her heart. She feared
The King might see the maiden. "Send away,"
She said, "the nurses and the women all."
Fair Bidasari wept when they retired.
The princess called her to her side and said:

"Thou must not weep so, Bidasari. They
Will all return. When thou dost wish to go,
They will go with thee. Now depart, *dyangs*.
Ye need not care for Bidasari more.
I will procure her dames of company
And servants. You may come from time to time."
So they arose, and, with prostrations, went.
The Queen conducted Bidasari then
Into a room and left her all alone,
And all afraid.   When evening shadows fell,
The great King bade the Queen to sup with him.
He sat beside her, smiled and gayly talked,
As he had been young Bedouwandas, on
His horse, with sword at belt. "My royal spouse,
How thou dost love me! for thou wouldst not sup
Without me, though thou needest food and drink."
Now when the King had eaten, he retired
Unto his sleeping-chamber.   Still alone
And weeping much, fair Bidasari stayed,
In darkness with no one to speak to her.
She thought on her dear parents. "O my God!
Why dost Thou leave me here?" The solitude
Filled her with terror, and she wept until
The middle of the night, and thought of home.
Out spake the King: "Now what is that I hear?
What voice is that so sorrowful and sweet?"
"It is an infant crying," said the Queen.
"In all the darkness it has lost its way."
Her heart was burning, and she sent a word
To Bidasari that she must not weep,
And held her peace and waited till the dawn.
But Bidasari wept the whole night long
And cried for home. When the *dyangs* all ran
To comfort her, they found the door was locked,
And none could enter. Bidasari thought,
"What wrong have I committed, that the Queen
Should be so vexed with me?" When day appeared,
To the pavilion went the King. The Queen

Threw wide the door of Bidasari's room
And entered all alone.
                  Then Bidasari
The Queen's hand kissed, and begged that she would let
Her homeward fare. " O gracious Queen," she said,
" Take pity on me; let me go away.
I'll come to thee again."
                  The wicked Queen
Struck her, and said, " Thou ne'er shalt see again
Thy home." The gentle Bidasari drooped
Her head and wept afresh, shaking with fear.
" Forgive the evil I have done, my Queen,
For I am but a child, and do not know
How I have sinned against thee," falling at
Her feet she said. The Queen in anger struck
Her once again. " I know full well," she said,
" All thy designs and projects. What! Am I
To rest in peace and see thy beauty grow,
And thee become my rival with the King? "
Then Bidasari knew 'twas jealousy
That caused the fury of the Queen. Her fear
Increased, she trembled and bewailed her fate.
The livelong day she was insulted, struck,
And of her food deprived.
                  Before the King
Returned, the Queen departed from the room
Of Bidasari. The poor child had lost
Her former color. Black her face had grown
From blows, as if she had been burnt. Her eyes
She could not open. Such her sufferings were
She could not walk. Then unto God she cried:
" O Lord, creator of the land and sea,
I do not know my fault, and yet the Queen
Treats me as guilty of a heinous crime.
I suffer hell on earth. Why must I live?
Oh, let me die now, in the faith, dear Lord.
My soul is troubled and my face is black
With sorrow. Let me die before the dawn.
My parents do not help me. They have left
Me here alone to suffer. In the false

Dyangs I trusted, as to sisters dear.
Their lips are smiling, but their hearts are base.
Their mouths are sweet as honey, but their hearts
Are full of evil. Oh, what can I say?
It is the will of God."
                              Such was the grief
Of Bidasari, and her tears fell fast.
Now when the King went forth again, the Queen
Began anew her persecutions harsh.
With many blows and angry words, she said:
"Why dost thou groan so loudly? Dost thou seek
By crying to attract the King, to see
Thy beauty? 'Tis thy hope, I know full well,
His younger wife to be. And thou art proud
Of all thy beauty." Bidasari was
Astounded, and replied with many tears:
"May I accurséd be if ever I
Such plottings knew. Thou art a mighty Queen.
If I have sinned against thee, let me die
At once. For life is useless to the hearts
That suffer. Hast thou brought me here to beat?
How thou hast made me weep! O Queen, art thou
Without compassion?"
                              All possessed with rage
The Queen replied: "I do not pity thee.
I hate thee, when I see thee. Open not
Thy mouth again." The wicked Queen then seized
The lovely tresses of the beauteous maid,
And took a piece of wood with which to strike;
But Bidasari wept and swooned away.
The King's voice sounded through the corridor,
As he returned. The Queen then hastened forth
And left a *mandar* there to close and guard
Fair Bidasari's room, that nothing should
Be seen. Then asked the King of her, "Whom hast
Thou beaten now?" The hypocrite replied,
"It was a child that disobeyed my will."
"Are there not others for that discipline?
Is it for thee to strike?" His *siri* then
He took, and kissed the Queen with fondest love.

All the *dyangs* fair Bidasari's plight
Observed, and kindly pity filled their breasts.
"How cruel is the conduct of the Queen!"
They said. "She made us bring her to her side
But to maltreat the child the livelong day.
It seems as if she wished to slay her quite."
Then secretly they went, with some to watch,
And sprinkled Bidasari's brow. To life
She came, and opened those dear wistful eyes.
"My friends," she said, "I pray ye, let me go
Back home again unto my father's house."
"Oh, trust in God, my child," said one in tears.
"My lot is written from eternity.
Oh, pray the princess great to take my life,"
The poor child cried; "I can no longer stand;
My bones are feeble. Oh, she has no heart!"
But the *dyangs*, for fear the Queen might see,
All fled.

Meanwhile the merchant and his wife
Wept all the day, and sighed for their dear child,
Sweet Bidasari. Nor did gentle sleep
Caress their eyes at night. Each day they sent
Rich presents of all kinds, and half of them
Were for the child. But naught the wicked Queen
To Bidasari gave. So five days passed
And then Dyang Menzara forth they sent.
The merchant said: "Oh, tell the mighty Queen
That I must Bidasari see. I'll bring
Her back in three days' time." The good
Dyang went to the queen and bowing low:
"The merchant fain would see his child," she said.
At this the features of the Queen grew hard.
"Did they not give their child to me? Now scarce
A day has passed, and they must see her face.
Is it thine own wish or the merchant's? I
Have said the girl could go where'er she would.
Can I not have her taken back myself?"
Then the *dyang* bowed, beat her breast, and went,
Sad that she could not Bidasari see,
And quaking at the anger of the Queen.

Of the *dyang*, fair Bidasari heard
The voice, and felt her heart break that she could
Not speak to her and send a message home.

Upon the morrow, when the King had gone
Among his ministers and men of state,
The Queen again to Bidasari's room
Repaired, to beat her more. As soon as she
Beheld the Queen, poor Bidasari prayed
To her, " O sovereign lady great, permit
That I may go unto my father's house."
The princess shook with rage, her face on fire.
" If thou but sayest a word, I'll slay thee here."
To whom could Bidasari turn? She bent
Before the will of God, and in a sweet
Voice said: " O Lord, my God, have pity now
Upon me, for the cruel world has none.
Grant now the Queen's desire and let me die,
For she reproacheth me, though naught I've done.
My parents have forgotten me, nor send
A word." The angry princess struck again
Her piteous face, and as she swooned away
A napkin took to twist into a cord
And strangle her. She summoned to her aid
Dang Ratna Wali. " Help me pluck this weed;
I wish to kill her." But the woman fled,
As base as cruel. Bidasari's ghost
Arose before her. Yet the child came back
To consciousness, and thought amid her tears:
"I'll tell the story of the golden fish
Unto the Queen, that she may know it all;
For I can but a little while endure
These pains." She spoke then to the Queen and said:
" O Queen, thou dost desire that I shall die.
Seek out a little casket that doth lie
All hidden in the fish-pond at our house.
Within it is a fish. Have it brought here
And I will tell thee what it signifies."
The princess called Dyang Sendari: " Go
And bring here the *dyangs*, with no delay,

From out the merchant's house." When they arrived:
" Go, now, *dyangs,* for Bidasari saith
There is a little casket in the pond
Where she is wont to bathe. Go bring it me,
In silence, letting no one see ye come."
Then the *dyangs* replied: " Oh, hear our prayer
For Bidasari. How her parents grieve!
Oh, pardon, princess, let her go with us."
The Queen with smiles responded: " The young girl
Is very happy here, and full of joy.
Her parents must not grieve, for in two days
If Bidasari doth desire to go
I'll send her freely. She is vexed that ye
Come here so often." The *dyangs* bowed low,
And smiled, and called enticingly: " Come forth,
O charming child, pure soul; it is not right
To treat us so, for we have come to see
Thy lovely face, and in its beauty bask."
Sweet Bidasari heard, and could not speak,
But answered with her tears. The cruel Queen
Said to them: " Speak no more. But if ye bring
The little casket, ye will fill the heart
Of Bidasari with great joy." Forth fared
Then the *dyangs,* and found the casket small,
And brought it to the palace of the Queen.
Again to Bidasari called the good
Dyangs: " Oh, come, dear heart, and take it from
Our hands yourself." " She sleeps," the princess said.
" Come back to-morrow." So they bowed and went.
The princess hastened with the casket rich
To Bidasari's room, and opened it
Before her eyes. Within it was a box
Of agate, beautiful to see, and filled
With water wherein swam a little fish
Of form most ravishing. The princess stood
Amazed to see with eyes of fire a fish
That swam. Then was she glad, and spoke with joy
To Bidasari: " Say what signifies
The fish to thee? What shall I do with it?"
Then Bidasari bowed and said: " My soul

Is in that fish. At dawn must thou remove
It from the water, and at night replace.
" Leave it not here and there, but hang it from
Thy neck. If this thou dost, I soon shall die.
My words are true. Neglect no single day
To do as I have said, and in three days
Thou'lt see me dead."
                              The Queen felt in her heart
A joy unspeakable. She took the fish
And wore it on a ribbon round her neck.
Unto the Queen then Bidasari spoke,
" Oh, give my body to my parents dear
When I am dead." Again the young maid swooned.
The Queen believed her dead, and ceased to beat
Her more. But she yet lived, though seeming dead.
The joyful Queen a white cloth over her
Then spread, and called aloud to the *dyangs*,
" Take Bidasari to her father's house."
They groaned and trembled when they saw that she
Was dead, and said with many tears : " Alas !
O dearest one, O gold all virginal !
What shall we say when we thy parents see?
They'll beat their breasts and die of grief. They gave
Thee to the King because they trusted us."
But the proud Queen, her face all red with hate :
" Why stay ye? Take the wretched girl away."
They saw the Queen's great rage, and bore the maid
Upon their shoulders forth, and carried her
Unto her father's house at dead of night.
Fear seized the merchant. " Say what bring ye here?
Tell me, *dyangs*." They placed her on the ground.
The merchant and his wife, beside themselves,
With tears embraced her form. " I trusted in
The Queen, and so I sent my child to her.
O daughter dear, so young, so pure, so sweet,
What hast thou done that could the Queen displease,
That she should send thee home like this to me?
How could the Queen treat Bidasari so?
For seven days she imprisoned her and sent
Her home in death. Ah, noble child ! alas !

Thy father's heart will break, no more to hear
Thy voice. Speak to thy father, O my child,
My pearl, my gem of women, purest gold,
Branch of my heart; canst thou not quiet me?
O Bidasari, why art thou so still?
Arise, my pretty child, arise and play
With all thy maids. Here is thy mother, come
To greet thee. Bid her welcome. Why art thou
So motionless? Hast thou no pity, dear,
To see thy father overwhelmed with woe?
My heart is bursting with despair because
Thou'rt lost to me."
                Long time the merchant thus
Lamented. "What have I to live for now?
Since thou art dead, thy father too shall die.
It is his lot both night and day to sigh
For thee. My God, I cannot understand
Why this dear child should thus a victim be!
'Tis the *dyangs* who have this evil wrought."
Then, through the whole *campong*, the merchants all
Made lamentations, rolling on the ground,
With noise of thunder, and their hearts on fire.
They sought to speak and could not. Then began
Again the merchant, and unto his friends
Told his misfortune, asking back his child.

The Queen's *dyangs* shed tears, and gently said:
" Speak not so loudly. Thou dost know that we
Are but poor servants, and we tremble lest
The Queen should hear. If any one of us
Had done this wrong, we'd tell it to the King.
Fate only is at fault. Oh, be not wroth
With us. Our will was good. We had no end
Except to see thy lovely daughter great
And powerful. Naught the King hath known of this.
It was the Queen's mad jealousy and hate."

The merchant and his wife accepted these,
The *dyangs'* words. " It is as they declare.

The Queen was jealous and embittered thus
Against our Bidasari. To your home
Return, *dyangs*. I fear me that the Queen
May learn of your delay and punish ye."
They bowed and went, with hearts of burning grief.

The merchant and his wife then lifted up
Poor Bidasari. They were all but dead
With sorrow. On his knees the father took
The body wrapped in crimson silk. He felt
A warmth. Then he remembered that within
The water was her vital spirit still,
And, placing her upon a mat, sent Dang
Poulam, the casket from the pond to bring.
But 'twas not there. Then all the household searched,
But found it not. The merchant beat his breast.
" Branch of my heart," he said, " we all had thought
Thou wouldst become a princess. I have lost
My reason. I hoped now to summon back
Thy spirit vital, but the casket's lost.
My hope is gone. It may be the *dyangs*
Have stolen it. They're faithful to the Queen.
We may not trust in them. They're filled with hate
And trickery." Unconscious all the time
Lay Bidasari; but at midnight's hour
She for the first time moved. They torches brought
And there behind Egyptian curtains, right
And left, ignited them, with many lamps'
Soft flames. The servants watched and waited there.
The father, always at his daughter's side,
With fixed glance looked for life to come once more
Back to his darling one. She moved again.
With opening eyes she saw and recognized
Her own soft couch, her parents, and her maids.
She tried but could not speak. Her hot tears fell,
She slowly turned and looked with fondest love
Upon her parents.
                          When the merchant saw
That Bidasari's spirit had returned,

He took her on his knees and gave her rice.
She could not walk because such pain she felt.
She thought upon the Queen and wept afresh.
They dried her tears, and placed within her mouth
What food she liked. The merchant tenderly
Said, " Bidasari, dear, what has thou wrought
To cause the Queen against thee thus to act? "
Young Bidasari, with a flood of tears, replied:
" No wrong at all I wrought the cruel Queen.
All suddenly her insults she began,
And beatings." They were stupefied to hear
Such tales. " Light of my eyes," the father said,
" We do not doubt thine innocence. Her deeds
Were those of madness. For her haughty birth
I care no whit. Wisdom and virtue bind
True hearts alone. As friends we ne'er must name
Those false *dyangs*. Not plants medicinal,
But poison foul, are they. These days are bad.
Injustice reigns. Believe me, friends, it is
A sign the last great day shall soon appear.
Those false *dyangs* are but a race of slaves,
Insensible to all that's good. The hour
The princess knoweth Bidasari lives,
We all shall die, the princess is so wroth.
Illustrious Queen they call her—but her words
Are hard and cruel. May the curse of God
O'erwhelm her and annihilate! From thee,
O God, she shall receive the punishment
Deserved. She who pursueth thus a soul
Shall know remorse and pain. So God hath willed.
So God hath willed. Who doth another harm
Shall suffer in his turn. It shall be done
To him as he hath done to others. So,
My child, my crown, have no more fear at all.
Intrust thyself to God. The cruel Queen
Shall yet be treated as she treated thee."
The merchant thus lamented till the night
Was half departed, shedding sapphire tears.
The innocent young girl, like marble there,

Slept till the evening twilight came. Toward dawn
She swooned anew.
     The merchant and his wife
Were much disturbed to see at night she came
To life, but when the daylight shone again
They lost her, and her spirit fled away.
This so distressed the merchant's heart, a lone
Retreat he sought to find. The parents cried:
" O dearest child, there's treason in the air.
Hatred and anger the companions are
Of lamentations and of curses dire.
Foul lies for gold are uttered. Men disdain
The promises of God, the faith they owe.
Oh, pardon, God! I ne'er thought the *dyangs*
Would thus conspire. But since they are so bad
And treated Bidasari thus, we'll go
And in the desert find a resting-place.
And may it be a refuge for us all,
Hidden and unapproachable.
        His goods
He gathered then, and all his servants paid,
And built a home far in the desert land,
A spot agreeable. A cabin there
He raised, with ramparts hemmed about, and strong
Sasaks, and seven rows of palisades.
They placed there many vases full of flowers,
And every sort of tree for fruit and shade,
And cool pavilions. This plaisance so fair
They called Pengtipourlara. It was like
The garden of Batara Indra. All
About, the merchant set pomegranate-trees
And vines of grape. No other garden was
So beautiful. 'Twas like the garden fair
Of great Batara Brahma, filled with fruits.
When all was ready, forth they went, toward night,
And took young Bidasari, and much food.
They fared two days and came unto the spot,
A garden in the desert. Softest rugs
From China there were spread and of bright hue

The decorations were, in every tint.
The house was hung with tapestries, and ceiled
To represent the heavens flecked with clouds.
And all about were lanterns hung and lamps.
Soft curtains and a couch completed this
Enchanted resting-place. Always the light
Was uniform, and brilliant as the day.
'Twas like a palace of a mighty king,
Magnificent and grand beyond compare.
There was a table on a damp rug set,
With drinks for Bidasari, and with bowls
Of gold, and vases of *souasa*, filled
With water. All of this beside the couch
Was placed, with yellow *siri*, and with pure
Pinang, all odorous, to please the child.
And all was covered with a silken web.
Young Bidasari bracelets wore, and rings,
And ear-rings diamond studded. Garments four
All gem-bedecked upon a cushion lay,
For Bidasari's wear. When night had come
Young Bidasari waked. Her parents dear
Then bathed her, and her tender body rubbed
With musk and aloes. Then she straight was clad
In garments of her choosing. Her dear face
Was beautiful, almost divine. She had
Regained the loveliness she erst possessed.
The merchant was astonished, seeing her.
He told her then that they would leave her there,
" Branch of my heart and apple of my eye,
My dearest child, be not disturbed at this.
I do not mean to work thee any harm,
Nor to disown thee, but to rescue thee
From death." But as she listened to these words
Young Bidasari wept. She thought upon
Her fate. Into her father's arms she threw
Herself, and cried: " Why wilt thou leave me here,
O father dearest, in this desert lone?
I'll have no one to call in case of need.
I fear to stay alone. No one there'll be
To talk to me. I only count those hours

As happy when I have my parents near."
The merchant heard fair Bidasari's words
And wept with his dear wife. With bitter grief
Their hearts were shattered. Counsels wise they gave
To Bidasari. " Dearest daughter mine,"
The father said, " gem of my head, my crown,
Branch of my heart, light of my eyes, oh, hear
Thy father's words, and be thou not afraid.
We brought thee hither, to this fair retreat,
Far from the town, for, if the Queen should know
Thou liv'st at night, the false *dyangs* would come,
And who against the princess can contend?
They'd take thee back, and thus exonerate
Themselves. I'd let myself be chopped in bits
Before thou shouldst unto the Queen return.
Thy father cannot leave companions here,
But after three days he will come to thee.
Thy parents both will soon come back again."
Then Bidasari thought: " My parent's words
Are truth, and if the Queen should find I live
She would abuse me as before. Give me
One maid-companion here to be with me,"
She asked. " My child, trust not," he said, " in slaves,
Nor servants, for they only follow pay."
Then Bidasari silence kept, and they,
The father all distraught and mother fond,
Wept bitterly at thought of leaving her.
Fair Bidasari bade them eat, before
They started. But because of heavy hearts
They but a morsel tasted. At the dawn
Young Bidasari swooned again. They made
All ready to return to town. With tears
The father said: " O apple of my eye,
Pearl of all women, branch of my own heart,
Pure gold, thy parents leave thee with distress.
No more they'll have a daughter in the house.
But, dear, take courage, we shall soon come back."
They left here with a talking bird to cheer
Her loneliness, close shutting all the gates
Of all the seven ramparts. Through a wood

Bushy and thick they took a narrow path,
In sorrow, but with confidence in God.
" O sovereign God, protect our child," they said.
When they had fared unto their house, they prayed
And gave much alms.
                              When evening shadows came
Young Bidasari waked, and found herself
Alone, and was afraid. With bitter tears
Her eyes were filled. What could she say? She gave
Herself to God. Alas, our destiny
Is like a rock. 'Twas hers to be alone.
It is in no man's power to turn aside
Or change whatever is by fate decreed.
All desolate sat Bidasari. Sleep
Wooed not her eyes. Now when he heard the cry
Of " Peladou," the owl lamented loud.
Upon her parents coming, loaded down
With dainties for the child, she for a while
Her woe forgot, and ate and drank with joy.
The little bird with which she talked upheld
Her courage with its soothing voice. So ran
The days away. Upon pretext he gave
Of hunting deer, the merchant daily came.

SONG III

H EAR now a song about the King Djouhan.
　　The wise and powerful prince e'er followed free
　　His fancy, and the Princess Lila Sari
Was very happy in her vanity.
Since she had killed (for so she thought) the maid,
Young Bidasari, tainted was her joy.
"The King will never take a second wife,"
She mused, "since Bidasari is now dead."
The King loved Princess Lila Sari well.
He gratified her every wish, and gave
Her all she asked, so fond was he of her.
Whene'er the princess was annoyed, the King,
With kisses and soft words would quiet her,
And sing to her sweet songs till she became
Herself again. "Poor, little, pretty wife,"
He'd say, and laugh her fretful mood away.
One night as he lay sleeping on his bed,
A dream tormented him. "What may it mean?"
He thought. "Ah, well, to-morrow morn I'll seek
An explanation." At the dawn he sat
Upon a rug Egyptian, breaking fast,
And with him was the princess. When she had
The dainties tasted, the *dyangs* arrived
With leaves of perfume. Then the King went forth
Into the garden. All the officers
Were there assembled. When they saw the King
They all were silent. To a *mantri* spoke
The King: "My uncle, come and sit thee here.
I fain would question thee." The King had scarce
These words pronounced, when, bowing very low,
The *mantri* in respectful tones replied,
"My greetings to thee, O most merciful
Of kings." He sat him near the throne. "I dreamed

Last night," the King continued, " that the moon
In her full glory fell to earth. What means
This vision?" Then the *mantri* with a smile
Replied: " It means that thou shalt find a mate,
A dear companion, like in birth to thee,
Wise and accomplished, well brought up and good,
The one most lovable in all the land."
The King's eyes took new fire at this. He said
With smiles: "I gave the Queen my promise true
That never I would take a second wife
Until a fairer I could find than she.
And still she is so lovely in my eyes,
Her equal cannot anywhere be found.
You'd take her for a flow'r. Yet when arise
Her storms of anger, long it takes to calm
Her mind, so waspish is her character.
The thought of this doth sadden me. Should one
Not satisfy her heart's desire, she flies
Into a passion and attempts to kill
Herself. But 'tis my destiny—'tis writ.
The Queen is like a gem with glint as bright
As lightning's flash. No one can ever be,
I tell thee now, so beautiful to me."
The *mantri* smiled. " What thou dost say is just,
O King, but still if thou shouldst someone find
More beautiful, thou yet couldst keep thy word.
The beauty of the Queen may fade away.
The princess thou shalt wed, O King, hath four
High qualities. She must, to be thy queen,
Be nobly born, and rich, and fair, and good."
The prince replied: " O uncle mine, thy words
Are true. Full many princesses there live,
But hard it is to find these qualities.
The Queen is good and wise and lovable.
I do not wish another wife to wed,
And wound the Queen with whom three years I've lived
In love and harmony. Yet if I saw
A quite celestial maid, perhaps I might
Forget, and marry her, and give the Queen
A gay companion." " O accomplished prince,

Thou sayest truly. Stay long years with her
Thy Queen, thy first beloved, for she hath all—
Great beauty and intelligence." They bowed
As forth from them the King went palaceward.
He sat beside the Queen, and kissed her cheeks,
And said: "Thy features shine with loveliness,
Like to a jewel in a glass. When I.
Must leave thy side, I have no other wish
But to return. Like Mount Maha Mirou
Thou art." The princess said: "Wherefore art thou
So spirited to-day? Thou'rt like a boy."
"Branch of my heart, my dearest love," he said,
"Vex not thyself. Thou know'st the adage old:
First one is taken with a pretty face,
Then wisdom comes and prudence, and, with these,
One loves his wife until the day of death.
If thus thou dost deport thyself, my dear,
My heart between two wives shall never be
Divided; thou alone shalt own it all."
The Queen was charmed to hear his loving words.
At night the Queen slept, but King remained
Awake, and watched the moon, and called to mind
His dream. As dawn approached he slept, and seemed
To hear an owl's shrill voice, like Pedalou's.
When it was fully day, the royal pair
Together broke their fast. The King went forth
And orders gave, in two days to prepare
A mighty hunt, to chase the dappled deer,
With men and dogs and all apparel fit.
Then back into the palace went the King,
And told the Queen, who straightway gave commands
For food to be made ready. At midnight
Behind Egyptian curtains went to rest
The King and Queen, but slept not. Still the dream
Was ever in his thoughts and worried him.
At dawn he said farewell unto the Queen.
She was all radiant, and smiling, said:
"Bring me a fawn. I'll tell the servants all
To take good care of it, so it may grow
Quite tame." "What we can do, my dear, we shall,

So all of thy desires may come to pass."
And so the King took leave, with kisses fond,
And, mounted on a hunter brown, set forth,
With velvet saddle decked with fringe of pearls.
Lances and shields and arrows and blow-guns
They bore. The wood they entered, and the beasts
All fled before their steps at dawn's first ray.
And when the sun was up, they loosed the hounds
With savage cries. Toward noon an animal
In flight they saw, and would have followed it,
But then up spake the King and said, " We are
So hot and weary, let us linger here
For rest." One-half the company astray
Had gone, each striving to be first of all.
The King, attended by a faithful three,
Reclined upon the ground, and sent them forth
For water. So the *mantris* went to find
A river or a pond, and faring far
To Bidasari's plaisance came at last.
They stopped astounded, then approached the place.
When they were near the lovely garden close,
They said: " There was no garden here before.
To whom does this belong? Perchance it is
A spirit's bower. No human voice is heard
But just the cry of ' minahs ' and ' bajans.'
Whom shall we call, lest spectres should appear? "
They wandered round the ramparts, and a gate
Discovered, shut with heavy iron bar,
And vainly tried to open it. Then one
Of them went back, and found the King, and said:
" Hail, sovereign lord, we have no water found,
But a *campong* here in the desert lone,
As splendid as a sultan's, with all sorts
Of trees and flow'rs, and not a mortal there.
'Tis girt about with double ramparts strong.
No name is seen, and all the gates are shut,
So that we could not enter."
                Scarce the King
Had heard the *mantri's* word when off he rushed
To see the fair domain. Before the gate

He stood astonished. "Truly, *mantris* mine,
It is as you have said. I once was here
And then the wood was filled with thorns and briers."
'Tis not a nobleman's *campong*. It must
Have recently been made. Now summon all
The *mantris* here and see what they will say."
They called aloud, "Oh, hasten, friends, and bring
The water here." Seven times they called, but none
Responded. Said the King, "It is enough.
'Tis like as if one called unto the dead."
"We'd best not enter," said the *mantris* then,
"It may be the abode of demons fell.
We are afraid. Why should we linger here?
Return, O King, for should the spirits come
It might to us bring evil. Thou shouldst not
Expose thyself to danger." But the King
Upon the *mantris* smiled. "Ye are afraid
Of demons, spectres, spirits? I've no fear.
Break down the barriers. I'll go alone
Within the precincts." When the gates were forced,
He entered all alone. The *mantris* all
Were terrified lest harm should come to him.
They sought with him to go. He lightly said:
"No, *mantris* mine, whatever God hath willed,
Must happen. If in flames I were to burn,
In God I still should trust. 'Tis only He
That evil can avert. We mortal men
No power possess. With my own eyes I wish
To see this apparition. Should it be
The will of God, I'll come forth safe and sound.
Be not disturbed. In case of urgent need
I'll call upon ye. All await me here."
The *mantris* made obeisance and replied,
"Go, then, alone, since thou hast willed it so."
Into the plaisance strode the King. He saw
That all was like a temple richly decked,
With rugs of silk and colored tapestries
Of pictured clouds and wheels all radiant,
And lamps and candelabra hung about,
And lanterns bright. 'Twas like a palace rich.

The eyes were dazzled with magnificence.
And seats there were, and dainty tables rare.
As through the palace went the King, the more
Astonished he became at all he saw,
But nowhere found a trace of human soul.
Then spake the little bird: "Illustrious King,
What seek'st thou here? This mansion is the house
Of ghosts and demons who will injure thee."
The King was filled with wonder thus to hear
A bird address him. But it flew away,
And hid behind a couch. "The bird I'll find,"
He said, and ope'd the curtains soft. He saw
Full stretched, upon a bed in dragon's shape,
A human form, in heavy-lidded sleep
That seemed like death, and covered with a cloth
Of blue, whose face betokened deepest grief.
"Is it a child celestial?" thought the King,
"Or doth she feign to sleep? Awake, my sweet,
And let us be good friends and lovers true."
So spake the King, but still no motion saw.
He sat upon the couch, and to himself
He said: "If it a phantom be, why are
The eyes so firmly shut? Perhaps she's dead."
She truly is of origin divine,
Though born a princess." Then he lifted high
The covering delicate that hid the form
Of Bidasari sweet, and stood amazed
At all the magic beauty of her face.
Beside himself, he cried, "Awake, my love."
He lifted her and said, with kisses warm,
"Oh, have no fear of me, dear heart. Thy voice
Oh, let me hear, my gold, my ruby pure,
My jewel virginal. Thy soul is mine.
Again he pressed her in his arms, and gave
Her many kisses, chanting love-songs low.
"Thou dost not wake, O dearest one, but thou
Art yet alive, because I see thee breathe.
Sleep not too long, my love. Awake to me,
For thou hast conquered with thy loveliness
My heart and soul." So fell the King in love

With Bidasari. " Ah, my sweet," he said,
" In all the world of love thou'rt worthiest."
The *mantris* grew uneasy at his stay.
They rose and said: " What doth the King so long?
If harm befell him, what would be our fate?
Oh, let us call him back at once, my lords."
So one approached the palace, and cried out:
" Return, O prince accomplished, to us now.
Already night is near. Back thou may'st come
To-morrow ere the dawn. We are afraid
Lest spirits harm thee. Come, O King, for we
A-hungered are, and wait for thy return."
But the illustrious prince was mad with love
Of Bidasari. Pensively he cried:
" Branch of my heart, light of mine eyes, my love,
Pure gold, thou'rt like angel. Now must I
Depart. To-morrow I will come again."
With no more words he left her, but returned.
" My heart would tell me, wert thou really dead.
Some trouble hast thou, dearest one? " he cried.
" What bitter grief hath caused thee thus to sleep? "
He found the nobles murmuring and vexed.
" O King," they said, " our hearts were filled with fear
Lest evil had befallen thee. What sight
So strange hath kept thee all these hours? " The King
Replied with laughter, " There was naught to see."
But they remarked his brow o'ercast with thought,
And said, " O King, thy heart is sorely vexed."
" Nay, nay," the King replied, " I fell asleep.
Naught did I hear except the *mantri's* voice.
It surely is the home of demons dread
And spirits. Let us go, lest they surprise
Us here." He seemed much moved. " We naught have
        gained
But weariness. So let us all go home
To-night, and hither come again at dawn.
For I a promise gave the Queen to bring
A fawn and a *kidjang*." The *mantris* said:
" None have we taken yet. But game we'll find
To-morrow, and will save a pretty fawn."

The King, when they returned, went straight within
The palace. There he saw the Queen, but thought
Of Bidasari. " O my love," he said,
" To-morrow I'm resolved to hunt again,
And bring thee back a fawn, and win thy thanks.
I'm never happy when away from thee,
My dearest love. Thine image is engraved
Upon my heart." Then he caressed the Queen
And fondled her, but still his heart went out
To Bidasari. All night long his eyes
He did not close in sleep, but thought of her,
In all her beauty rare. Before the dawn
The royal couple rose. The King then gave
Command that those who wished should hunt again
With him. At sunrise forth they fared.

On Bidasari let us look again.
When night had gone, in loneliness she rose,
And ate and drank. Then to the bath perfumed
She went, and coming to her chamber, took
Some *siri* from the betel-box. She saw
A *sepah* recently in use and cast
It forth. She thought within herself:
" Who could have used it? Someone hath been here."
She ran through all the rooms, but nothing found
Except the *sepah* in the betel-box.
" Had it my father been, he would have left
Some food for me. Oh, he is very rash
To leave me here alone." Upon the couch
She sat and wept, and could not tell her grief
To anyone. " When we no longer may
Live happily," she said, " 'tis best to die.
My parents never can forgiven be,
To leave me here like any infidel.
And if I suffer, they will sorrow, too."
The *minahs*, the *bajans*, and talking birds
Began to sing. She took a 'broidered cloth,
And 'neath its folds she sweetly fell asleep.

The King's horse flew apace to the *campong*
Of Bidasari. All the *mantris* said:

"Thou takest not the path for hunting, sire;
This is but the *campong* of demons dread
And spectres. They may do us deadly harm."
The great prince only laughed, and made as if
He heard not, still directing his fleet course
To Bidasari's garden, though they sought
His wishes to oppose. When they arrived
Before the palisades, the *mantris* cried:
"Avaunt, ye cursed demons, and begone
Into the thorns and briers." Then to the King:
"If thou wilt prove the courage of thy men,
Lead us behind the barriers, among
The evil spirits. We will go with thee."
"Nay. Let me go alone," the prince replied,
"And very shortly I'll come forth again."
They said: "O prince, to us thy will is law.
To God most high do we commend thy soul."
Alone the prince in Bidasari's home
Set foot. He was astonished, for he saw the bath
Had recently been used, and all the lamps
Were trimmed and full of oil. Then opening
The chests, he saw the traces of a meal,
And glasses freshly drained. The chambers all
He searched, and came to Bidasari's couch,
And, lifting up the curtains, saw her there,
Asleep beneath the 'broidered covering.
"'Tis certain that she lives," he said. "Perchance
It is her lot to live at night, and die
At dawn." Then came he nearer yet, and gazed
Upon her beauty. Ling'ring tears he saw
Bedewed her lashes long, and all his heart
Was sad. Her face was beautiful. Her locks
Framed it with curls most gracefully. He took
Her in his arms and cried, with kisses warm:
"Why hast thou suffered, apple of my eye?"
He wept abundantly, and said: "My gold,
My ruby, my carbuncle bright, thy face
Is like Lila Seprara's, and thy birth
Is pure and spotless. How could I not love
A being fair as thou dost seem to me?"

Thy beauty is unspeakable; thou art
Above all crowns, the glory of all lands.
My soul adores thee. Lord am I no more
Of my own heart. Without thee, love, I could
No longer live; thou art my very soul.
Hast thou no pity to bestow on me?"
The more he looked the more he loved. He kissed
Her ruby lips, and sang this low *pantoum:*

SONG

Within a vase there stands a china rose;
 Go buy a box of betel, dearest one.
I love the beauty that thine eyes disclose;
 Of my existence, dear, thou art the sun.

Go buy a box of betel, dearest one.
 Adorned with *sountings* brave of sweet *campak*,
Of my existence, dear, thou art the sun;
 Without thee, everything my life would lack.

Adorned with *sountings* fair of sweet *campak*,
 A carafe tall will hold the sherbet rare;
Without thee, everything my heart would lack;
 Thou'rt like an angel come from heaven so fair.

A carafe tall will hold the sherbet rare,
 Most excellent for woman's feeble frame.
Thou'rt like an angel come from heaven so fair,
 Love's consolation, guardian of its flame.

At the approach of night the *mantris* said,
" What doth the King so long away from us?"
They were disturbed, the prince seemed so unlike
Himself and filled with such unrestfulness.
" I fear me much," then said a *mantri* there,
" That some mishap hath overwhelmed the King.
Perhaps by some bad spirit he's possessed,
That he to this weird spot should fain return."
One went and cried: " Come hither, O our King!
The day declines; we've waited here since dawn."

The King responded to the call, and came
With smiling face, though pale, unto the gate:
" Come here, my uncle; come and talk with me,
Thy King. No evil thing hath come to pass."
" O lord supreme, most worthy prince, return.
If harm should come to thee, we all should die."
" Be calm, my uncle, I will not this night
Return, but he may stay with me who wills."
" O King, with spirits what hast thou to do?
Thy face is pale and worn, and tells of care."
The King but sighed, and said: " My heart is full
Of trouble, but the will of God is good.
Here yesterday a fair celestial form
With angel face I saw. 'Twas here alone."
And so the King told all that had occurred.
" Go back," he added. " Leave me here with her.
Say to the Queen I've lingered still a day
For my amusement, with my retinue."
Then half the escort stayed, and half repaired
Back to the palace to acquaint the Queen
The King would stay another day and hunt.
When all was dark, sweet Bidasari waked
And saw the King, and tried to flee away.
He seized and kissed her. " Ruby, gold," he said,
" My soul, my life, oh, say, where wouldst thou go?
I've been alone with thee for two whole days,
And all the day thou wrapped in sleep didst lie.
Where wouldst thou go, my dove?" The gentle girl
Was much afraid and trembled, and she thought:
" Is it a spirit come to find me here?
Avaunt thee and begone, O spectre dread,"
She said, amid her tears. " No phantom I,"
Replied the King; " be not afraid. I wish
To marry thee." Then Bidasari strove
Again to flee. Then sang the King a song
That told of love and happiness. Its words
Astonished Bidasari, and she cried:
" Art thou a pirate? Why dost thou come here?
Speak not such things to me. If thou shouldst be
Discovered by my father, he would cut

Thee into pieces. Thou shouldst go alone
To death, and find no pardon in his heart.
Take all my gems and hasten forth at once."
The King replied: " 'Tis not thy gems I want,
But thee. I am a pirate, but thy heart
Is all I want to steal. Should spectres come
In thousands, I would fear them not at all.
No tears, my love, bright glory of my crown.
Where wouldst thou go? Hast thou no pity, sweet,
For me? I am a powerful prince. Who dares
Oppose my will? Pure gold, all virginal,
Where wouldst thou go?" So spake the King, and fair
Young Bidasari trembled more and more.
" Approach me not," she cried, " but let me bathe
My face." " I'll bathe it for thee, dear," he said.
But Bidasari threw the water pure
Into his face. " Not that way, child," he laughed;
" My vesture thou hast wet. But I shall stay
And meet thy parents here. Oh, hearken, love.
I followed far the chase, and wandered here.
I sought a pretty fawn to take the Queen;
But now thy face I've seen, no more I wish
To go away. Oh, have no fear, my child;
I would not harm thee. When thy parents come,
I'll ask them for thy hand. I trust they'll grant
My prayer. I'll lead thee forth from this fair spot
Unto my palace. Thou shalt sit beside
The Queen, and live in happiness complete."
Sweet Bidasari bowed her head and wept,
All red with modesty. Unto herself she said:
" I never thought it was a king. How rude
I was! I hope the King will not be vexed."
He calmed her fears with tender words of love.
" Branch of my heart," he said, " light of my eyes,
Have no more fear. Soon as thy parents fond
Have given their consent, I'll lead thee forth.
My palace is not far. A single day
Will take us there. It is not difficult
To go and come." Then Bidasari knew
It was the King of that same land. With fright

She nearly swooned at thought of all the woe
The Queen had caused her. " O my lord," she said,
" I'm but a subject humble. Give me not
The throne. I have my parents, and with them
Must stay." The King was overjoyed. " My dear,"
He said, " by what names are thy parents known?"
With low, sweet voice the tender girl replied:
" Lila Djouhara is my father's name.
He dwelleth in Pesara." " Dearest one,
Tell me the truth. Why have they treated thee
In such a fashion—why abandoned thee
In solitude? Thy father is not poor.
A merchant rich is he, of birth, who hath
A host of slaves and servants. For what cause
Hath he his daughter left in this far spot?
He is renowned among the merchants all,
Both good and honest. What hath forced him here
Within this lonely wood to hide thee, dear?
Oh, tell me all; let nothing be concealed."
She thought: " It was the fault of his own Queen.
But if I tell him all—he never saw
Me there, within the palace—should he not
Believe, I'll be a liar in his eyes."
She feared to speak and tell him of the Queen.
She thought, " So cruel was the Queen to me
When she but feared a rival, what would come
If I should sit beside her on the throne?"
Then in her sweet voice Bidasari said:
" My glorious King, I am afraid to speak.
I am not suited to a royal throne.
But since thou lovest me, how dare I lie?
If thou dost favor me, the Queen will vex
Her heart. My parents fear her. 'Tis the cause
Why hither they have brought me. Three long months
Ago I came, for terror of the Queen."
She thought on all the horror of those days,
And choked with sobs, and could no longer talk.
Then tenderly the King spake to the girl:
" Ah, well, my darling love, confide in me
The secret thy dear heart conceals. Fear naught;

The Queen is good and wise, and knoweth how
To win all hearts. Why should she render thee
Unhappy? Speak not thus, my pretty one;
The Queen could never do an evil deed.
When thou art near her, thou shalt see, my dear,
Whether she loves or hates thee."
                                    At these words
Young Bidasari knew the King esteemed
The Queen, and felt her heart sink in her breast.
" My words are true," she said, " but still perchance
My prince cannot believe. But was I not
Within thy palace six or seven nights?
The sweat of pain became my couch, so great
Was my desire to see my parents dear.
They sent me dainties, but all the *dyangs*
Were kept as prisoners by the princess there.
She said she'd take me back herself. One day
I was, indeed, sent home, but scarce alive."
She told him everything that came to pass.
He listened stupefied, and said: " How could
It be that thou wert in the palace hid,
And I not see thee there? Why was it thou
Wert not beside the Queen? I've never left
The palace for a single day. Where wert
Thou hid? Thy strange words I believe, my dear.
Speak without fear and let me know the whole."
Urged by the King, young Bidasari told
Him all. And when the conduct of the Queen
He learned, the King was wonder-struck. A rage
Most terrible possessed him. But his love
For Bidasari mounted higher still
And his compassion. " So the Queen thus wrought!
I never thought hypocrisy could be
So great! I never in the princess saw
Such bent for evil. But be not, my dear,
Disconsolate. It is a lucky thing
Thou didst not quite succumb. No longer speak
Of that bad woman's ways. Thank God we've met!
So weep no more, my love. I'll give to thee
A throne more beautiful than hers, and be

Thy dear companion until death." " O King,"
She said: " I have no beauty fit to grace
A throne.   Oh, let me stay a simple maid,
And think of me no more."   The King replied:
" I will not give thee up.   But I must still
Return, and meditate how I may win
Thee back to life complete."   With kisses warm
He covered her fair face.   She bowed her head,
And silence kept; and when the morning dawned
She swooned anew.   It was a proof to him
That she had told the truth.   A mortal hate
Then filled the prince's heart against the Queen.
Touched with deep pity for the maiden young,
He kissed her once again, and left her there,
So white and still, as if she lay in death.
What of the *mantris?*   They awaited long
The King, in silence.   Then the oldest said:
" O sovereign lord, O caliph great, wilt thou
Not now return? "   " I'll come again, dear heart,"
He said, and sought the city.   Straight he went
Into the palace, to the Queen, who asked:
" What bringest thou from hunting? "   He replied
In murmurs: " I have taken naught at all.
For my own pleasure I remained all night."
" 'Tis nothing, lord, provided no harm came
To thee.   But say what thou didst seek, to stay
So long?   I always have prepared for thee
The food for thy great hunts, but never yet
Have I received a recompense? "   The King
To this replied with smiles: " Prepare afresh,
For I to-morrow shall depart again.
If I take nothing, I'll return at once."
As he caressed the Queen, upon her breast
He felt the little magic fish of gold
All safe.   Then gave he quick commands to all.
" I'll hunt to-morrow, and shall surely bring
Some wondrous game."   Now when the princess fell
Asleep he found upon her heart no more
The little fish.   " 'Tis as the maiden said,"
He thought.   " The princess hath a wicked soul.

With such a heart I cannot go with her
Through life." Through all the night he could not sleep,
But thought upon the girl. He was as sad
As though he heard a touching song. At dawn
The royal couple rose and went to bathe.
The King into the palace came again
And sat upon the throne adorned with gems.
He donned the royal robe to wear before
The dear young girl. A vestment 'twas of silk,
All gold embroidered, with a tunic bright,
Of orange hue. His mien was most superb,
As doth become a mighty king. He bore
A quiver of Ceylon, most deftly wrought.
When all the *mantris* had assembled there,
The King within the palace once more went
And met the Queen. Caressing her he took
The little fish that lay upon her breast.
The princess wept, and at the door she cried:
"Why takest thou my little ornament?"
The great King gave no heed, and went away,
At dawn's glad hour, when birds begin to sing.
Swords gleamed and lances shone, and through the wood
They hastened on, with quivers and blow-guns,
And seemed a walking city.
                               Now again
To Bidasari let us turn. When dawn
Appeared, she rose and sat in loneliness,
Her face grew still more beautiful. Her state
Astonished her. "Perhaps it is the King
Who hath this wonder wrought. How happy I
To be no longer dead!" She washed her face
And felt still sad, but with her pensiveness
A certain joy was mingled, for her pain
Was passed. Her grief the "talking bird" allayed
With songs about the mighty King and love.

Song

There's *siri* in a golden vase,
   Good Dang Melini plants a rose;
The King admires a pretty face,
   To-day he'll come to this fair close.

Good Dang Melini plants a rose,
 Here in the garden they will meet;
To-day he'll come to this fair close,
 To man and maiden love is sweet.

Here in the garden they will meet,
 Go seek the fairest fruit and flower;
To man and maiden love is sweet,
 The King is coming to the bower.

Lo! At this very instant they approached.
Dear Bidasari hid behind the couch.
The King searched everywhere, and found at last
The maiden hiding, bathed in bitter tears.
Then kissing her, the King inquired: " My love,
Bright glory of my crown; pray tell to me
Why thou art sad." He dried her tears. But she
Still hung her head in silence. Then the King
For elephants and horses to be sent
Gave orders. " Go with *mantris* two at once,
And bring the merchant and his wife, and bid
Forty *dyangs* to hasten here forthwith."
Then went the *mantris* forth in haste, and found
The merchant and his wife and said, " The King
Inviteth ye to come." Then through the wood
The parents hurried to the plaisance fair
Of Bidasari, there to meet the King.
Before his Majesty they bowed with fear.
The great King smiled. " Be not afraid," he said,
" My uncle and my mother. Let us go
Within, to see thy lovely child. I make
Ye now my parents. We have friendly been,
And still shall be." Beside the King they saw
Fair Bidasari seated, as with steps
Still hesitating they the palace sought.
The father fond was glad within his heart,
His daughter was so beautiful. She seemed
A princess lovely of the Mount Lidang.

"Dear Bidasari, sweetest child," they said,
"Behind the King, dear daughter, thou should stand."
She made as if to go, but still the King
Restrained her. "No, my pretty one," he said,
"Thy place is at my side. So God hath willed."
The oldest *mantri*, called for counsel, spoke:
"Lila Djouhara good, what sayest thou?
Art thou not glad to see thy daughter made
A queen? What happiness hath come to thee!"
The merchant bowed before the King, and said:
"Make her thy servant, not thy wife, my lord.
Thy glorious Queen we fear. She e'er hath shown
For Bidasari hatred dire, because
A child so lovely might attract the King."
The monarch hearing him thus speak, still more
Toward him was borne. "My uncle," then he cried,
"Have no more fear. But never shall I make
A servant of thy daughter."

                              Then he gave
Command to build a castle in the wood.
And all the workers came, and built it there,
With ramparts three. As if by magic then
A golden palace rose. The outer gate
Was iron, loaded down with arms, and held
By demons and by Ethiopians.
These were the keepers of the gates, with steeds
Untamed. With swords unsheathed they stood alert
And waited for the King's commands. Of brass
All chiselled was the second gate, supplied
With cannons and with powder, guarded safe
By beings supernatural. The third
Was silver, such as may be seen in far
Eirak. The beauty of the castle was
Beyond compare! From far it seemed to be
As double, like an elephant with two
White ivory tusks. Where may its like be found?
Three diamonds pure reflected all the light,
Big as a melon. Now the castle built,
The King a plaisance beautiful desired

With gay pavilions, and all kinds of plants.
The middle booth nine spacious rooms displayed,
One for the royal audiences, adorned
And pleasant as a bed of flowers.

                              The King
A festival maintained for forty days,
With games and sports and dances to divert.
And never was such animation seen!
All ate and drank to sound of music sweet.
They passed the loving-cup and drank to each
In turn.

            For forty days resounded there
The gongs and *gendarangs,* and joyous tones
Of gay *serouni* and *nefiri* glad.
"How beautiful is Bidasari!" all
Exclaimed; "a thousand times more lovely than
The Queen." Thrice happy are the merchant now
And his good wife; by marriage they're allied
To our great King, though strangers to the land.
We count it strange that Bidasari's face
In naught is like the merchant nor his wife.
Who knoweth but that she, in mortal shape,
An angel fair may be? Full many slaves
The merchant hath, but never children own."
"He found her when a babe, upon the shore,"
Another said, "and brought her up."

                              The King
Heard all their words. He thought: "It is the truth
And this I take as proof of her high birth.
She certainly is noble or come down
From heaven."

                  When four days had fled, the wives
Of *mantris* dressed the beauteous girl. They clad
Her form in satins soft of Egypt, shot
With gold, adorned with precious stones inset
And many gems. Her beauty was enhanced
The more, till she a radiant angel seemed.
She wore a tunic, crimson and pomegranate,
With buttons shaped like butterflies. She was

Adorned with *padaka* of five quaint clasps,
And belt called *naga souma*. Ear-rings rich
She had, of diamonds set in gold, and wrought
Most wondrously, as bright as daylight's gleam;
A ring most marvellous and rare she wore
Called *astakouna*, and another named
Gland kana, and a third from far Ceylon,
Studded with precious stones. Her eyes were like
The stars of orient skies. Her teeth were black,
Her face like water shone. Her chiselled nose
Was prominent and like a flower fresh culled.
When she was dressed, upon a couch of pearls
Her mother put her. Supple was her form,
And white, as she reclined, by many maids
Surrounded. In his royal garb the prince
Was clad, and dazzling to the eyes of all
Who saw. He wore a kingly crown which shone
With diamonds bright and lucent amethysts
And many stones, and all majestic seemed.
Then rice was brought. The King with pleasure ate
And what was left he gave the *mantris'* wives.
When all had finished he perfumed himself
And gazed upon his lovely wife. Her face
And form were charming. Her soft tresses curled
In grace. Her eyes still kept the trace of tears,
Which made her lovelier. The silken folds
Of soft Egyptian curtains fell. They were alone.
" Awake, my darling," said the prince at dawn,
" Crown of my life, awake, my pretty one."
Then Bidasari waked and said, with tears:
" My friend, I had all sorts of wondrous dreams.
I saw a palm-tree tall with tufted limbs,
And fruits all ripe." When three days more had fled
And all the people saw and loud acclaimed,
Then Bidasari took the rank of Queen.
The King o'erloaded her with gifts and loved
Her tenderly. "Oh, let us live and die
Together, dear, and, as the days go by,
Think more of one another, and our love
Preserve, as in the hollow of the hand

Oil is upheld, nor falls a single drop."
So spake the King.

             The merchant and his wife
Were soon established in the neighborhood,
Near to Queen Bidasari's palace grand.
A hundred servants had they to fulfil
Their orders. They sent gifts to all their friends,
And food to last a month.

                  A certain day
It chanced that Bidasari said: " O King,
Why goest thou no more within the gates
Of that thine other palace? Of a truth
Queen Lila Sari will be vexed, because
Thou hast abandoned her so long a time.
She'll think that I have kept thee from her side
Unwilling thou shouldst go." So, with all sorts
Of words, fair Bidasari strove to urge
The King to visit Lila Sari. " I
Will go to-morrow," finally he said.
He went, when morning came, and met the Queen.
She turned him back, and with sharp, bitter words
Reproached him. " Wretched one, I will not see
Thy face. I love thee not. I hate thee. Go!
Lila Djouhara's son-in-law, thou'rt not
To me an equal. Thy new wife's an ape,
Who liveth in the woods."

                But when the King
Heard these vociferations of the Queen,
He said: " Branch of my heart, light of my eyes,
Oh, be not vexed, my dear. It was not I
Who wrong began, but thou didst cause it all.
For thou didst hide thy deed from me, and drive
Me on to this extremity. Oh, why
Art thou now angry with me? If thou wilt
But love her, and attach thy heart to hers,
She'll pardon thee, and take thee as a friend."
As more and more enraged the Queen became,
Her wrath with strong reproaches overflowed.
" Depart from here, accursed of God! Thou art
No longer husband mine. Go live with her

Whom God hath struck, but whom thou dost delight
To honor.   Formerly of noble blood
Thou wert, but now no more than broken straw.
Thou needst not further try to flatter me.
Though thou shouldst purify thyself seven times, false one,
I'd not permit thee to approach my side."
The King grew angry and replied: " 'Tis thou
Who art despicable.   Thy cunning tricks
Are worthless now.   Thy jealousy insane
Was without cause, and common were thy acts.
Thy wit is much below thy beauty.   Ill
Will follow thee, should I protection cease."
" Have I forgot my noble birth? " she asked.
" But thou hast erred, to lower thine high estate
To people of such base extraction.   Here
And everywhere thy shame is known, that thou
Art wedded to a gadabout.   Is it
For princes thus to wed a merchant's child?
She ought far in the woods to dwell, and know
Most evil destiny."   The King but smiled
And said: " If this event is noised abroad,
'Tis thou who wilt receive an evil name.
For who in all the land would dare prevent
The King from marrying?   I ought to take
From thee all I have given.   But before
The people I've no wish to humble thee.
Is it because I met thy every wish
That thou art grown so bad?   Most evil hath
Thy conduct been, and I with thee am wroth,"
And in hot anger rushed the King away,
And straight repaired to Bidasari's side.

SONG IV

THIS song will tell again about the prince
    Of Kembajat, most powerful. He was chased
    By fell *garouda*, horrid bird of prey,
And sought another land. His way he took
Toward Indrapura. At the break of dawn
A daughter fair was born, a princess true,
Within a boat that lay upon a shore.
The Queen and he abandoned her, and went
Back to the royal palace and for days
Bemoaned her fate. Of her they nothing heard.
" Alas my child!" the father cried, " my dear,
In whose care art thou now? We do not know
If thou art dead or living. Thus thy sire
Hath no repose. Light of mine eyes, my love,
My purest gold, our hearts are torn with grief.
An evil fate was ours to hide thee there.
We do repent the deed. To think that thou
Perchance hath fallen among the poorest folk!
A slave perhaps thou art!" The prince's son
Remarked the sorrow of his parents dear,
And was profoundly moved. " Have I," he asked,
" A sister? Tell me why have ye concealed
Her far away? Did ye not care for her?
Was she a burden that ye must forsake
Her thus? Doth shame not fill your parents' hearts?"
But when he heard the tale in full, he said:
" O father, let me go to seek for her,
My sister dear. If I succeed I'll bring
Her back to thee." " Oh, leave us not, my son,"
The father said. " Thou art our only heir.
Like a tamed bird upon our shoulders fain
We've carried thee, and watched thee, day and night.
Why shouldst thou leave us now? Oh, go not forth.

55

Vex not thyself about thy sister dear.
From travellers we shall get news of her,
And her abode discover."
　　　　　　　　　　　Then the prince
Bowed low and said: "My father, lord, and King,
I am but strengthened in my wish to go
And find my sister.　Let me now depart,
And seek for news of her."　The King replied:
"Well, go, my dearest son; thy heart is good.
Though but a child thou still dost bear a brain."
Then summoned the young prince the merchants all,
And bought much goods and questioned them in turn
About all neighboring villages and camps.
They told whate'er they knew most willingly,
For much the young prince was beloved by them.
Among them was a youth of handsome face,
Fair Bidasari's foster-brother tall.
Amid the strangers sat he near the throne;
His name was Sinapati.　He was brave
And wise.　Now as he watched the prince he thought,
"How strangely like dear Bidasari's face
Is his, as when a reed is split in twain
There is no difference between the halves."
His home he left when Bidasari fair
Became the Queen.　He thought of her and wept.
The prince observed him there, and said, with smiles:
"Young man, my friend, from what far town art thou?
Why dost thou weep so bitterly?　What thoughts
Arise in thee and make thy visage dark?"
Young Sinapati bowed and said: "My lord,
I came from Indrapura, in a ship,
My wares to sell.　For that I do not weep.
But sorrow cometh to my heart whene'er
I think upon my home, and brothers dear,
And sisters."
　　　　　　　At these words the prince rejoiced.
He thought, "From him some news I'll surely learn."
Sherbets and dainties then to all the folk
He offered, and the cup went 'round from dawn
Till noon, and then the merchants went away;

But the young prince kept Sinapati there.
Now he already strong affection felt
For him and said: " My friend, toward thee I'm moved
And look upon thee as a brother dear.
Thou dost at Indrapura live, but who
May be thy patron there?" Then with a smile
Young Sinapati said: " My patron's called
Lila Djouhara, merchant great. He owns
Some six or seven swift ships, and toileth more
Than ever since he Bidasari took
As child." In two days' time the young prince went
With Sinapati to his father's house.
" I bring thee news," he said, "but nothing yet
Is sure. Behold from Indrapura far
A youth, from whom I've things of import great.
A merchant of Pesara, very rich,
My sister must have found. All well agrees
With what to me thou saidst. Now must we seek
For confirmation of the glad report."
To Sinapati gold and gems they gave.
Then spake the King: " If this be so I'll send
An envoy bearing richest gifts, and thanks
Within a letter writ."
                              The youthful prince
Bowed low and said: " Oh, send me on this quest!
Lila Djouhara I would like to see.
Perhaps he's virtuous and just. If I
Am made full sure it is my sister dear,
I'll send a messenger. And if it be
I'll bring her back."
                              The King was moved
To hear his son thus speak. " O dearest child,"
He said: " I'm very loath to let thee go.
But thou must many horsemen take with thee,
Lest thou shouldst long be absent."
                                          " Why should I
Be long away?" the prince replied, with bows;
" For if Lila Djouhara will not let
Her come, I shall forthwith return to thee."
The King could now no more object. He gave
Vol. 49—17

Commands to make an expedition great.
With richest gifts, and food, and princely things,
And sent him forth with blessings on his head.
" Stay not too long ; thou art my only hope,"
The King exclaimed ; " I'm getting old, my son,
And thou my heir upon the throne must be."
They started early on the fourteenth day
Of that same month. And Sinapati rode
Beside the Prince.

        Some went on foot and some
On horses. When they far had gone, the prince
Said to the youth : " Now listen, friend. When we
Arrive thou must not name my family
And rank. I'm someone from another town.
It doth not please me to declare my rank
To strangers. Should the girl my sister prove,
Thou mayst tell all, for I shall soon return."
Thus speaking, the young prince his way maintained,
And soon arrived near to the city sought.
He Sinapati left, and went within
The gates, with four companions, true as steel,
And six attendants. They at once repaired
To the *campong* of good Lila Djouhara.
They found it closed, with a forsaken look.
" There's no one here. The King hath taken all
Away, both old and young," said the *mandar.*
Then Sinapati beat his breast and said :
" What hath become of my dear patron, then ? "
" Be not disturbed. No harm hath come to him.
The merchant with the King hath gone, because
The King hath married Bidasari fair,
And made of her a queen, and built a fine
New palace in the country wild. There all
Is joy and happiness." Beyond all count
Was Sinapati glad to hear these words.
Then to the prince he said : " My gracious lord,
Lila Djouhara's near at hand. He is
In highest favor with the King, and bears
A title new." They hurried forth to find
His residence. " It is the left *campong*,"

Remarked a country-man. "Thy lord is grand
And powerful now, and master of us here.
The King hath now become his son-in-law."
Then Sinapati went within the gates
And saw his mother there. Her heart was touched.
She kissed him and inquired, "Whom hast thou brought?"
"It is a friend," he answered. "Come, my lord,"
She to the young prince said, "enter and rest."
"He's so like Bidasari," to herself
She said. "What is thy name, my brave young man,
Thou seemest nobly born. In very truth
Thou'rt handsome and well mannered." Then the prince
Said: "Poutra Bangsawan I'm called. Thy son
I've followed here." But Sinapati paid
Him homage, and they knew him for a prince.
Before his door young Sinapati slept
At night to guard him safe. Next day there came
An invitation from Lila Mengindra
(Before, Djouhara). So they started forth.
Lila Mengindra was astonished quite
To see the prince's face so beautiful.
"Who is this most distinguished stranger here?"
He asked himself. "My master, speak a word
To Poutra Bangsawan, a friend of mine,"
Said Sinapati. So the old man turned
And spoke unto the prince, "Come here, my son,
And sit thee near thy father." He felt drawn
To him, he looked so much like Bidasari.
The young prince smiled and on the dais sat.
"What is thy visit's purpose?" then inquired
The good old man. The prince with bows polite
Replied: "I'm but a humble stranger, come
To find my sister. I bespeak thine aid."
"Be not afraid, my son, but trust in me,
Nor fear to give thy sister's name. If thou
Wilt have it so I'll take thee for a son;
I love thee for thou hast a face so like
My daughter's." Then the brave young prince began
And told his sister's story, how she was
In time of stress abandoned on the shore.

" And if I only knew," he said, " where now
She is, I'd be her master's willing slave."
Now when Lila Mengindra heard his tale
His joy was quite unspeakable. His love
For Bidasari's brother greater grew.
With smiles he asked: " Now, Poutra Bangsawan,
Say of what family thou art, that I
May aid thee in thy quest, and help thee find
Thy sister." Then the young prince bowed his head
And pondered, " Shall I lie?" For he knew not
If 'twere his sister. Lila saw his mood
And said: " Be not disturbed. It is most sure
That thy dear sister's here. So speak the truth,
That my old heart may be surcharged with joy.
Thy sister's seated on a throne, and like
A brilliant jewel is her family.
Be no more sorry. As for me, my heart
Is full of joy."
        The prince looked in his face
And said: " Can I confide in him? I am
A stranger here and fear to be deceived."
Said Sinapati: " Speak not thus, I pray,
For everybody knows this man can tell
Ten-carat gold from dross. Now list, my lord.
Although he bids me silent be, a prince
He is, son of a powerful king, and comes
To seek his sister." Then within his heart
The former merchant much rejoiced, as if
He'd found a mountain of pure gems. He paid
His homage to the prince in proper form,
And took him into his abode, to meet
His wife and all within. The spouses two
To him exclaimed: " Dear prince, in our old age
We're very happy. When thy sister sweet
We found, o'erjoyed were we. And now the King
Hath married her, and raised her to the throne.
He hath our family to noble rank
Upraised, and covered us with benefits."
Then smiling said the prince: " I learn with joy
My sister sweet is here. When may I go

Before the King and see her? For I've come
To take her home. And yet I fear the King
Will never let her go away from him.
When I have seen her I'll return again."
In three days' time the King gave audience.
The former merchant with him took the prince,
Who sent the richest presents on before.
The princeling was most gorgeously attired
And bore himself with haughty dignity.
His robe was rich, his tunic violet
And fire. His many-colored turban bore
Bright agates. At his girdle hung his *kriss*.
He was entirely clad as prince should be,
And bracelets wore with little bells and rings.
His leggings were embroidered with bright flowers
Called *pouspa angatan*. He seemed divine—
His beauty was extraordinary. Pearls
In numbers countless covered all his garb;
An amulet he had with sacred verse
From the Koran, a diamond pure. He rode
A steed most richly housed, with *shabraque* decked
With gleaming jewels casting rays of light.
'Twas thus the prince set out to meet the King.
Lila Mengindra with him went. The prince
Approached the King's pavilion, and at once
The King remarked his beauty and his mien
Of noble grace. "Who can he be?" he thought.
Meanwhile the prince dismounted and appeared
Before the King. Full seven times he bowed
And said, "O may your happiness increase,
Illustrious sovereign!"

    Then the King with smiles
Lila Mengindra questioned, "Who is this
Thou hither bringest, of such noble mien
And amiable face?"

    With humble bow
The former merchant said: "This slave of thine
Has come from lands remote, from Kembajat,
Upon the seashore, since thy Majesty
He wished to see. His presents few he sent

Before him, which he hopes thou wilt accept."
The former merchant thought: "I would his rank
Divulge. But some might think I lied because
The King hath Bidasari wed, and if
She knew she was a princess born she might
Be very vain and haughty."
                                   To the prince
The King was very friendly. "Come and sit
Here by my side," he said, "for thee I deem
A brother." "Let me here remain, my lord,
I am a poor unworthy servitor.
I hope that thou wilt pardon me. I would
I might become a subject of thy crown."
The King thought: "This may be some royal heir
Who here hath wandered. He resembles much
Our Bidasari. Pity 'tis that he
Unto another nation doth belong."
Then pleasantly he said: "Pray, truly tell
What is thine origin? Keep nothing back.
What is thy name? The whole truth let me know."
The young prince bowed him low and said: "My name
Is Poutra Bangsawan, of family
Most humble. I am searching everywhere
To find a sister lost. When she is found
I shall return at once." Then said the King:
"Where is thy sister? I will help thy search.
Stay here with me a month or two, that we
May learn to know each other and become
Fast friends." The young prince then obeisance made
And said: "I bear thine orders on my head.
Thou art a king illustrious, and I
A humble servitor. I am the son
Of good Lila Mengindra, but for long
I've absent been. My sister dear I seek.
Thine aid I do bespeak. From Kembajat
I come, a subject of thy father there, the King.
Forgive me, lord, for now thou knowest all."
The King rejoiced to hear a voice that seemed
So much like Bidasari's, and inquired
Of Sinapati, "Tell me now his race."

Then Sinapati bowed and said: " My lord,
Of princes and of caliphs is his race.
His kingdom, not so far, is most superb;
His palace is most beautiful and grand.
Swift ships within the harbor lie, all well
Equipped." At this the King enchanted was,
To find a prince was brother to his wife.
Still more he asked and Sinapati said:
" Because his realm was ravaged by the foe
He hath misfortunes suffered manifold."
Then knew the King he was of royal blood
And had adversity experienced.
The King came from his throne and said, " My friend,
My palace enter." So the King and prince
Went in. They met fair Bidasari there.
She sat beside a Chinese window quaint,
All choicely carved. She saw the King and thought,
" What fine young man is this he bringeth here? "
When they were seated all, the young prince looked
At Bidasari: " Beautiful is she,"
He thought, " my sister dear, and very like
My father." Then the King with smiling face
Said: " Bidasari, darling, speak to him.
He is thy younger brother, come to seek
Thee here. From Kembajat he came. And thy
Dear father mourns for thee the livelong day."
At this fair Bidasari sighed. She bowed
Her head and silence kept. She much was moved
Because she had not known her parents true,
But fancied them Djouhara and his wife.
" I'm but a merchant's daughter," finally
She said. " Things all uncertain this young prince
Hath told. If I'm the daughter of a King,
Why hath he left me here, and never sought
For me through all these years? 'Tis not so far
From here to Kembajat." The young prince bowed.
" Thy words I bear upon my head," he said,
" O sister dear. Pray banish from thy heart
All hatred. If thou'rt lowly born, I am
Likewise. Our realm was ravaged at thy birth.

But shortly afterward fair peace returned,
And to his own my father came again.
I've seen how much he suffers in his heart.
Thy name he never utters without tears—
He never hath forgotten thee. Forgive
Him, then, in what he was remiss. Except
For stern necessity he never would
Have thee abandoned."
                              Then the King with smiles
Said: " Speak to him, my dear. He tells the truth.
Thy parents wandered through a desert land
Beneath a cruel sun. Impossible
It was to carry thee through brier and brush."
Down at his sister's feet the young prince knelt.
Then Bidasari clasped him in her arms.
The brave young prince to them recounted all
The sorrows of his parents. Much he wept,
And they wept, too, as he the story told.
Then sat they down to dine. And afterward
They *siri* took and perfumes of all kinds.
Then the young prince took leave. " Where goest thou,
My brother?" asked the King. " I fain would go
Straight home to my dear parents," said the prince.
But, with a voice affectionate, the King
Replied: " Seek not Lila Mengindra. Here
Thou shouldst remain, for thou hast met within
This palace thy dear sister. There is room
Enough for thee. Stay here with all thy folk
And retinue." The prince bowed low, and forth
Unto the merchant went, and to him said:
" Within the palace now I shall remain
With all my retinue, for thus the King
Commands." The merchant said: " 'Tis very well
For where can one lodge better than within
The palace?" So the prince returned, with all
His people, to the palace of the King.
Then all the *mantris* came, and festivals
And feasts were held. As long as he remained
At Indrapura, the young prince received
All courtesies. And Bidasari fair

Was known as daughter of a mighty king.
The news was carried far and wide, and all
Repeated how her brother brave had come
To seek for her.
       Queen Lila Sari heard
And was surprised. She sighed in solitude,
And felt a woe unspeakable. She said
To a *mandar:* " I was in too much haste.
On the *dyangs* I counted, but they come
No more. All four have gone and homage paid
To Bidasari. All my tricks are foiled.
In no one can I trust." Dang Lila then
Approached and said: " Acts of unfaithfulness
Bring never happiness. God's on the side
Of loyalty. Now those *dyangs* are sad
And languish after thee, but fear the King,
Dost thou not think, O Queen, thou ill hast wrought?
For while the King is absent none will come
Thy heart to cheer." The Queen replied with ire:
" Seek not to consolation give. The King
Esteems me not. I'll not humiliate
Myself before him. Who is that young prince,
So called, who hither came? A pirate's son
He well may prove, and calls himself a prince.
Go ye, *dyangs*, pay service to the King,
And he may favor ye as he did her."
She seemed most wroth. But she repented sore
In truth, and pined away in sorrow deep.
In other days she had no wish nor whim
Unsatisfied. Now all were for the King.
The Queen's heart angrier grew from day to day
As if a scorpion's sting had wounded her.
And her distress grew greater when she thought
Upon the love of other days. Her heart
Was inconsolable because so bitterly
She missed the pomp and glory of her court.
But Bidasari to the King one day
Said: " Send back these *mendars;* for if they all
Stay here, Queen Lila Sari all alone
Will be." The King with smiles replied: " Oh, no!

I will not let them go.   She is so fell
And barbarous, she no one loves.   She is
Much better all alone."   Then to the King
Fair Bidasari said: "Thine anger was
Too prompt.   She spoke in wrath because she was
Accustomed to a court.   In what to thee
Hath she been wanting, that thou shouldst repel
Her thus?   Thou gav'st her love, and now thou dost
Abandon her in sorrow.   Be not thus
Incensed with her, for should she come to want
The shame would be reflected on thy head."
The King's face lighted, and he said: "My dear,
I went to see her, but she drove me forth
With bitter words.   Her conduct was beyond
All bearing.   And she heaped on me abuse."
But Princess Bidasari said: "Dwell not
On that, my friend.   She was disturbed by wrath
And jealousy.   In other days thou didst
Embrace and kiss her.   Now she is alone.
And thou perchance didst somehow hurt
Or bruise her body."   All his anger left
The King at this.   He said: "O purest soul,
Thou speakest well and wisely.   How could I
Not love thee, dear, and cling to thee for life?
Oh, never may we separated be!
Branch of my heart, light of my eyes, thou dost
But good desire.   Thou'rt all the world to me.
I'll go to her, since thou doth ask.   Perchance
A reconciliation may be made.
But she must first admit her faults.   If she
Repentance shows, to see her I will go."
The merchant's wife had come and heard these words.
Her warm tears fell.   She thought within herself,
"My daughter hath no vengeance in her heart."
Then Dang Bidouri brought delicious rice
Unto the King and Queen.   They ate and drank,
And stronger grew their love from hour to hour.
Then gave the King commands to call the prince.
He came with smiling face and graceful bows.
"Sit here beside us," said the King, and all

The three dined there together, royal ones,
Surrounded by deft servants and *dyangs*.
They chatted gayly, and, with laughter, ate.
When all was finished, from the betel-box
The King of *siri* took, perfumed himself,
And then the prince retired.

                      When two short months
Had fled, the prince bethought him of his home
And parents.   To himself he said, " I'll go."
He gave commands to preparation make
For his departure.   " I am loath to leave
My sister," he to Sinapati said.
" My life is joyous here.   But there at home
I've left my parents in solicitude."
Then Sinapati bowed and said, " With thee
I'll go."

SONG V

ACERTAIN day the *mantris* came
Before the King, in the pavilion grand.
And with them came the youthful prince, and cast
Himself before the throne. The King with smiles
Said: "Sit thou at my side, my brother dear,
I have not seen thee for a day entire."
The princeling bowed and said: "My gracious lord
If thou wilt pardon me, I would return
And give my parents dear the joyful news.
My father bade me seek my sister lost,
And still he nothing knows of her good fate."
The King replied with sorrow: "Brother mine,
Why wilt thou go so soon? We scarcely are
Acquainted, and I have not had enough
Of thy dear company." The prince replied:
"Oh, be not sorrowful, my gracious lord.
As soon as I have my dear father seen
I'll tell him what good things have come to pass.
'Twill soothe his heart to hear my sister's joy.
My parents will be glad in learning all
Thy goodness great. And pray consider me
Thy subject leal. Soon I'll return again."
The King's emotion grew. With pleasant voice
He said: "Take counsel of thy sister. Heed
What she may say." They found the Queen within,
Fair Bidasari, and attending her
Dyang Agous Djouhari. All sat down
And took some *siri* from the betel-box.
The Queen to the young prince then spoke: "Come here.
My brother, why have I thy face not seen
For two long days?" With bows the prince replied:
"I've had a multitude of things to do.
Thus came I not; for my companions all

Seek homeward to return. So I must take
My leave of thee upon the morrow morn,
When pales the silver moon before the dawn."
The Queen was grieved to hear these words, and shed
A flood of tears. Her tender heart was touched.
Beside herself with sorrow she exclaimed:
" O prince illustrious! How canst thou go,
Since we have met? I've loved thee from the time
I knew thou wert my brother. I am grieved
To hear thee say thou wilt so soon depart.
Of low extraction must I be! 'Twas wrong
For thee to call thyself my brother. I
A poor and feeble orphan am, and how
Should I the love deserve of a great prince? "
When this he heard the prince bowed low his head
And was much troubled. " Sister sweet," he said,
" Grieve not like this. I only do return
Because our parents must so anxious be.
I love thee so, my darling, that my heart
Is nearly breaking. If thou speakest thus
To me, my dear, my grief will still increase.
I could not leave thee, but I must respect
Our parents' wishes. They commanded me
All haste to make. So—sweet—I pray thee have
Compassion on me."

                   Much disturbed, the King
Observed the sorrow of the princess fair.
He kissed her lips, to her a *sepah* gave,
And said with tender voice: " My darling wife,
What dost thou wish? Let now thy brother go.
We'll see thy parents here ere many days."
The Queen wept bitterly, and said to him:
" His wishes I do not oppose. Let him
Do whatsoe'er it pleaseth him to do.
For I am but a stranger, a lost child,
And who should think of me or love me true? "
Then bowed the prince and said: " In very truth,
I know thou art my sister. Speak not thus.
God knows how much I love thee, sister mine.
If thou dost not permit me to depart

I'll not resist.   I'm happy here with thee,
But our dear parents are in cruel doubt,
And look for news of thee.   Now that I know
Thy husband is a king, our parents dear
Would be so overjoyed to learn it too! "
Then spoke the King with face all radiant,
" Return not, brother mine," he said.   " I'll send
Swift messengers to bear the gladsome news
That Bidasari's found.   Then, if he wills,
Thy royal father here we'll hope to see.
I'll go myself to meet him when he comes."
The young prince bowed and said: " Nay, rather send
Thy messengers, a great king cannot go
So far away."   Queen Bidasari heard
These words and much rejoiced, and gayly gave
Her brother then her betel-box.
                                        The King
Caressed his wife and said, " My dearest soul,
Love not thy brother more than me."   He called
Lila Mengindra.   Soon the merchant came
Before the King and prince.   The King exclaimed:
" Come here, my uncle.   Tell me, wilt thou take
A letter to the King of Kembajat—
To prove to him we live? "
                                        So spake the King
And called his counsellor of state, who came
And kissed his hands.   The King then bade him write
A letter, all in characters of gold.
" Well," cried the King, " let's hear the letter now."
" Now glory be to God," it thus began,
And all fair Bidasari's history
Recited.   Then the King a mighty host
Assembled and with elephants and steeds
Ten *mantris* took the letter of the prince
Unto his parents.   With the cavalcade
There went a *laksimana* great, who bore,
As king's ambassador, bejewelled flags
And standards rich, and presents of much worth.
Then Sinapati by the King was called
A *laksimana mantri,* and received

A fine equipment, with a hundred men
To follow him. 'Twas thus the King preserved
His reputation as a mighty king.

When he had sent the embassy, the King
Went to his wife, and they were very gay.
His love for her grew greater every day.
The former merchant also was beloved.
He gave the King good counsel, and obeyed
His orders willingly. He often dined
Together with the King and Queen. His wealth
Grew vast. No one at all could with him vie,
In Indrapura. He was much attached
To the chief *mantri*. They were equals both
In prudence, wisdom, and fidelity,
With power unquestioned over all the folk.
Beneath their sway prosperity increased,
And many merchants came from far and wide.
The kingdom was at peace. The King rejoiced,
And everyone was happy in the land.

SONG VI

THE *laksimana mantri* now I'll sing,
    Who went upon the embassy. As soon
    As the great King of Kembajat had news
Of his arrival, he was much rejoiced.
He told the Queen, and in the audience-hall
Awaited. Then went forth the officers
With elephants and *payongs*. A countless throng
Attended them, with music and with flags.
They met the embassy, and, with rich gifts,
They gave the King's commands. Into the town
Then entered all. The King was very glad,
As if his only daughter had returned.
All bowed before the King, who took the gifts,
While servants took the letter to the chief
Of *mantris*. And he gave it to the King.
The monarch read, and was possessed with joy.
He could not thank enough the merchant good,
Who raised his daughter to a royal throne.
He wished forthwith to go and see his child.
The letter cordial invitation gave.
But one thing troubled him: " He straight inquired,
' Hath not the prince, my son, the liberty
To come back home?' " The *laksimana* bowed
And said: " The King wished not to let him come
And begged with tears that he would stay. The Queen
Feared if her brother went she'd never see
Her father. From your children both I bring
Warm greetings. Kind indulgence from your heart
They ask, and press their invitation. I
Crave pardon for myself, O King, and hope
Thy children dear may see their father's face,
And that the kingdoms may become one realm."
At these words smiled the King. " Ah, well!" he said,

72

" I'll wait for seven days still." Then questions flew,
And the great king learned all about his child.

The Indrapura *mantris* went apart
When evening came. A separate palace grand
The King assigned them, with the best of food.
He orders gave for preparations great.
Unto the Queen he said: " In seven days' time,
My dear, I look to start, for I shall have
No peace until I've seen our darling child."
Then he assembled there his *mantris* all,
Both young and old, with elephants and steeds.
And all was ready to set forth, as he had wished.
The while the morning stars were twinkling still,
The royal gong resounded many times.
The guards leaped forth with joy. The officers
Came out and took their shining helms of war.
Their naked swords all glistened. It was thus
They made the glittering royal cavalcade.
Their flags and banners flaunted in the air,
All those who stayed behind were sad, as if
A knife had cut them. All together marched,
The lancers and the horsemen, and they seemed
A moving city. Soon all darkened was
The moon, as someone sorrowful. The swords
And lances glistened like an island in
The middle of the sea. Thus is described
The royal escort marching through the land.
The King was mounted on an elephant,
His *siri*-bearer seated close behind.
A rich *payong* of royalty, all tricked
With bells, was stretched above his head,
And drums and other instruments without
Cessation sounded. Thus went forth the King,
And soon to Indrapura came.
                              When near
He halted and forthwith an envoy sent
His coming to announce, together with
The *laksimana mantri*. " Mighty King,"
They said, " thy royal father hath arrived."

The King his heralds ordered then to call
Lila Mengindra. With a smile he said
To him: " Assemble in the square the folk
And army. Straight to my pavilion let
Them come, and all in holiday attire,
For I my father am to meet to-day."
Lila Mengindra bowed and hied him forth
To execute the orders of the King.
The King within his palace went, and sat
Upon a jewelled seat. The Queen was there,
And good Lila Mengindra at her side.
The King said smilingly: " Light of my eyes,
Let all the palace decorated be.
Assemble all the palace folk and all
The younger girls. For now without the gates
Our parents wait. To-morrow I shall go
To meet them." Then Queen Bidasari cried,
With smiles: " My brother they have come to see.
I cannot go before them and declare
Myself their daughter." But the young prince said:
" Oh, speak not thus, my sister, but give heed
To what I say to thee, and be not wroth.
If I'm the only one they love, alone
I'll go with them away." Then to the King
He said: " With my dear sister I but jest,
To quiet her alarms." He bowed before the King
And asked permission forth to go at once
To meet his father. " Nay," replied the King,
" We'll go together." A repast was served
With every kind of food. The royal three
Together ate. Then from the betel-box
They _siri_ took, and perfumes sweet they used.
The prince then from the palace forth did go.
Next day the King invited him to start
With him upon the royal progress. All
The banners waved, and everyone was glad.
Then to the Queen he said: " Stay here, my love,
And I will hither bring thy father dear."
These words rejoiced the Queen. She said: " Go forth,
My dear, and I will follow with my eyes."

The King then took his leave with the young prince,
With many *mantris* following. The strains
Of gladsome music sounded. All the bells
Were rung, and those without the cavalcade
Were sad.
            Ere long they came to the frontier,
And King met King. The folk of Kembajat
Were all astonished at the young King's face,
As beautiful as painter's masterpiece.
The old King looked with smiles on all. His joy
Was great. The King of Indrapura bowed
Respectfully, and made them bring to him
The elephant that bore 'neath gay *payong*
His consort's father. "Son, where goest thou?"
"I've come to seek thee." Then the old King said:
"Why didst thou come in person? 'Twould have been
Enough if thou hadst *mantris* sent instead."
His joy o'erflowed his heart. His son-in-law
He greatly loved. Upon his elephant
He said: "Approach, my son, thou art a king
Renowned. Thy body and thy soul are both
Alike, and both of royal stock!" He pressed
Him in his arms and said: "Light of my eyes,
Almighty God hath heard my many prayers,
And granted me a perfect son-in-law."
The King of Indrapura bowed and smiled
Most graciously. Then to the young prince said
His father: "Mount, my son, beside me, here."
The young prince mounted at his father's side.
He was as beautiful as chiselled gold.

Within the town the kings made entry then
Amid a joyous throng. When they had come,
The former merchant bowed before them both,
The *mangkouboumi* now. The mighty King
Of Indrapura bowed and said: "My sire,
Speak to my uncle here; for he brought up
Thy daughter." Scarcely had the old King heard
These words than he exclaimed with joy: "Come here,
My brother, let us now acquaintance make."

The old King, seated on his elephant,
Shed all about him rays of happiness,
And all the people there were greatly moved.
" This is my brother well beloved," he said,
And kissed his brow. " How great hath been his love,
His faithfulness has proved beyond compare."
The former merchant bowed, and to the King
Replied: " I am thy slave, O King, and bear
Thine orders on my head. Thou dost o'erwhelm
Thy servant with thy favor." Then upon
The royal throne, which was all gem-bedecked,
The old King sat, the young prince at his side,
With all the *mantris* near. Then came the Queen
Consort. The prince and Bidasari fair
Came from their seats, their mother to receive.
All entered then the palace. The young Queen,
Fair Bidasari, bowed and was embraced
By both her parents. With a flood of tears
Her father said: " Alas, my darling child,
Fruit of my heart, light of my eyes, keep not
A hatred in thy soul against us now.
The will of God is now made manifest.
We long have separated been. At last
We see each other with our very eyes.
Great wrong we did thus to abandon thee,
But still let not thy heart a stranger be
To us. Peace later came to our dear land—
Such was our destiny. What could we do?
We were in flight. We thought, ' May God decree
Some honorable man shall find her here!'
How can we now be glad enough 'twas thus
Ordained! What recompense can we present?"
Sweet Bidasari wept as she recalled
The past. The King her husband was much moved,
And felt great pity when her tears he saw.
And all were sad with sorrow mixed with joy,
Because they knew she was of royal birth.
Food now was served, and quickly the *dyangs*
Brought salvers for the princes. The two kings
Ate of the rice till they were surfeited,

Then to their children offered it. All took
The *siri* placed before them, and straightway
Themselves anointed with rare perfumes sweet.
When all had eaten, the five royal ones
Lila Mengindra called, and gave to him
The remnants of the feast. The kings then spoke
To him and to his wife. They both bowed low
And kissed the royal hands. Then said the King
Of Kembajat: " My children, I had planned—
In case we ever met on earth and ere
The prey of death became—a feast to give,
To last a month, and to it ye invite.
In triumph I my daughter fain would bear,
With all of ye. I would at once repair
Unto the isle of Nousa Antara,
And there I'd hold a royal festival
With all the members of our family,
And all the *bitis, mandars,* and *dyangs.*
Such was my plan—if ever I should find
My daughter dear. Now while this moon doth last
Let me the project see fulfilled before
Your parents come to die."
                                    The gracious King
Of Indrapura at these words bowed low
And said: " I bear thy words upon my head.
It shall be done as thou hast wished, my King."
And when the evening came all was prepared.
Soft mattresses were spread, and the two queens
Betook them to their chambers, and the rich
Egyptian curtains fell. They vainly sought to sleep.
They talked together of their sorrows past
And evil days. And neither kings nor queens
That night could slumber.
                                    At the break of day
The talking bird began to sing and prate.
A little later the *bajangs* began
Their song. Then all arose, and bathed, and broke
Their fast, and chattered and amused themselves.
The King of Indrapura then gave word
Unto the *mangkouboumi:* " All prepare

That's necessary, ere the moon be full.
Get ready all the various kinds of ships,
And load them down with every sort of arms.
Prepare all sorts of games to pass the time,
And get in order all the cannons great
And fire-arms. Thus the King commands."
                                        Straightway
The *mangkouboumi* bowed before the King,
And went his orders to obey. He made
The ships all ready, with new paint and gold.
When three were well equipped, on board he took
The people of the city. All the old
Were left behind, but of the young none stayed.
Then to the King the *mangkouboumi* said,
" All is prepared." At this the King rejoiced,
And to the King of Kembajat sent word,
Who told his wife, and she was all aglow.
They started from the palace, kings and queen
And prince, and lovely Bidasari, too,
Attended by the courtiers all. The strains
Of music sounded and the bells were rung.
All those whose lot it was to stay at home
Were pained, as if a knife had stricken them.
The cannons roared ; the royal banners waved.

In three days' sail they reached the island fair,
Of Nousa Antara, and the ships made fast.
The two queens sat and watched the deft *dyangs*
Take up the coral white and pink, and toyed
With pretty shells. The King set foot upon
The isle of Nousa Antara. The King
And his dear wife upon the shore came forth,
With their sweet daughter Bidasari pure.
The King of Indrapura with them went,
The prince walked near them on the left.
                                        The King
Of Indrapura ordered that a tent
Be raised, and one was made. It was as large
As any palace, set with royal throne.
The two queens entered it and sought repose.

The prince before his father bowed and said,
" My royal father, let me go and hunt."
To this the King of Kembajat replied,
" Do what thou dost desire, light of my eyes."
The King of Indrapura said with smiles,
" I'll go with thee to hunt, my brother dear."
The prince replied, " I shall in truth be charmed,
My brother." " Forth we'll fare to-morrow morn,"
Returned the King of Indrapura. " Call
The folk together."

              When the dawn appeared,
The King and prince together started forth,
Escorted by a band of hunters tried,
And beat the woods for game. The King and prince
And all their following made rapid work.
The game took flight. The King then drew his bow
And many animals were killed. A deer
Came running by. His arrow struck him full
Upon the shoulder, and the huntsmen seized
And quickly killed him. In the pathless woods
Of Nousa Antara there was much game.
A tiger roared, the King and prince pursued.
The tiger swiftly fled. The prince sat down
Within the forest deep. To overtake
The beast he was unable. To return
He sought, but could not find the way. Alone
He was, and in perplexity, because
His huntsmen he no longer could descry.
Then, wandering to and fro, he found at last
A pleasure garden of the days gone by,
Belonging to King Lila, beautiful
And without flaw. He was astonished quite
When he perceived a palace. All alone
He found himself, when he had entered there.
He walked about, but found no living soul.
Unto himself he said: " Can this domain
A habitation be of demons dread
And spirits? Can this be the cause of all
The solitude which reigns?" On all sides then
He looked. All suddenly a voice he heard,

But still no one could see. Amazed he stood.
The mystic voice exclaimed, " Have pity, lord,
And free me from this room." As in a dream
The prince these accents heard. He answered then:
" Who art thou? Whose strange voice is this I hear,
The while I no one see? Dost thou belong
Unto the race of demons and of spectres?
Where is the key, that I may ope the door? "
Then the *dyang* of Mendoudari said
Unto the prince: " Look toward the left, for there
The key thou'lt find that opes the palace tower."
He took the key and opened wide the door.
All those who were within, when they beheld
The prince's face, fell prostrate at his feet.
To them the prince cried out: " Say to what race
Ye do belong. This quickly tell. And whose
This palace beautiful? " Then answered him
Dang Tjindra Melini: " O Royal prince,
We are God's creatures, like to thee. And this
Fair palace of the King Lila is now
By Ifrid occupied, a spirit-king,
With whom now lives the prince illustrious,
Lila. His daughter, Princess Mendoudari,
Is shut alone within a chamber here,
And Ifrid, king of spirits, cometh oft.
On every third day cometh he. His eyes
Are brilliant as the sun." When this he heard
The prince was glad. The room he entered then.
The Princess Mendoudari sought to flee.
" Where wouldst thou go, my friend," he said. " I've sought
And found thee. Do not flee away from me."
The Princess Mendoudari said with tears:
" And art thou mad enough hither to come?
The spirits will destroy thee without doubt."
These words rejoiced the prince, and to her then
He sang a low sweet song of love and wooing.
The princess answered with a dreamy chant.
And when the young prince heard her gentle lay
He felt a yearning pity for her fate.
" Be not afraid, my dear," he said, " for I

Will triumph over all thine enemies."
Then Dang Sendari served them dainty food;
And what was left, to her the princess gave.
The prince too *siri* from the betel-box
And rare sweet perfumes used. When evening came,
A soft couch for the prince was spread. And then
The princess sought her room, and curtains drew
Of rich Egyptian stuff. The prince had asked,
" When comes the spirit-king? " And she had said,
" At early dawn." The young prince could not sleep,
But through the long night hours sang soft *pantoums*.
When daylight came the prince arose. He heard
A spirit coming to the palace. Then with fear
Was seized the princess fair. " Behold," she cried,
" He cometh." Then the young prince took his arms.
" Fear not," he said; " have confidence in God.
What he decrees must always come to pass.
If I'm destroyed, then follow me in death.
I only ask one thing of thee, my love.
When I am dead, I pray thee weep for me,
And let thy mantle be my winding-sheet.
Now let thy glances follow as I go."

I'll tell of Ifrid now—the spirit-king.
He lurked beneath the palace. When he heard
The princess talking with the prince his ire
Arose like burning flame. His cry was like
A thunder-burst. The very palace shook.
" Depart from here," unto the prince he roared,
" And feel my mighty power." Then sweet love-songs
Exchanging with the princess went he forth.
His mien was like Sang Samba's, and his face
Was nobly firm, as if he went to meet
A roaring tiger. At his side he wore
A rare carbuncled sword, and arrows bore
With points in deadly poison dipped. Ifrid,
The creature with two heads, like spectre came
With laughter horrid. He took up a stone
And hurled it at the prince, who dodged its flight.
Then full of wrath Ifrid upon him rushed.

But swift the prince let fly an arrow sharp,
And pierced his heart. One groan, and then he fell,
And died beside the river. Then the prince
Made haste to join the princess.
                                        When she saw
The spirit Ifrid dead she much rejoiced
And bowed before the prince. Great gladness shone
In her fair face, because her woe had ceased,
And she was happy that 'twas to the prince
She owed her rescue. 'Twas as if she'd found
A mountain great of jewels. Then she said:
" Caliph a high divinity once was
And called himself King Lila. God will bless
Thee for thy deeds, O mighty prince."
                                        The prince
With kisses said: " Thou hast a charming mouth.
Thy form is supple. Prithee tell me why
I should not love thee? Thou art beautiful
As a statue of pure gold, and thou shalt be
A princess in my palace. Well I know
Thine origin is noble, and thy race
Is high." They gayly chatted while some food
Was served. The prince, with pleasure, at the side
Of the fair princess ate. When all was done
He took some *siri* from the betel-box
And perfumes used. " Thou art a jasmine sweet,"
He said, " an antidote to every ill,
And thou shalt be my wife."
                                        Next day the prince
Took her behind him on his horse, and they
Departed. The *dyangs* accompanied them.

Now will I tell about the *mantris* all.
Until the fall of evening, with the King
Of Indrapura, they in waiting stayed,
To welcome back the prince. And much disturbed
They were that he delayed so long to come.
The King then bade them seek the prince, and see
Why he remained so long apart from them.
Then *mantris* four set out, and hunted far

And wide, but found him not. They brought the news
That he could not be found. The King was sad
And ordered them to go and tell the King,
His wife's dear father, that the prince was lost.
The old King fainted when he heard the tale.
With oil of rose they sprinkled him, and back
Unto his senses came he. "O my child,"
He said, "my heart hath lost all hope. Where now
Art thou? I'll go, myself, to seek."

        The King
Wept much, and his dear wife. And as for her—
Sweet Bidasari—she appeared to wish
To kill herself, for never on the earth
Did brother love his sister like the prince
And Bidasari. At the fall of day
Back came the King of Indrapura, sad
And weeping. Then the King of Kembajat
Said: "O my son, be silent. Do not weep,
For thou dost but increase the pain I feel."
But Indrapura's King replied: "Alas!
He was my brother true, so brave and good!"
But while they were lamenting thus the prince
Stood there before them with his consort fair.
He bowed to all. The King, his father, saw
And could not speak. He thought, "It is the voice
Of my dear son." Then recognition came
And he was wild with joy. The prince then told
How he had chased the tiger, and had lost
His way within a wood: how he had killed
A spirit there, Ifrid, the dread.

        The King
Heard all he said and much rejoiced. Then came
The servants serving tasteful food to all.
The King ate with his wife and children dear.
Together they were six. All sorts of rare
And dainty food were served them, and the King
Took *siri* from the betel-box, and used
Sweet perfumes. The great King of Kembajat
Then gave a festival which lasted quite
Seven days, with music and diversions gay.

Glad joy was at its height, of pleasure born
And of the dance. The kings amused themselves.
All kinds of games they had. Intji Bibi,
A singer of Malacca, sang with grace.
The seven days passed, the Princess Mendoudari
Was all in finery arrayed. The wives
Of the two kings took her in hand. The prince
Was by the *mangkouboumi* ta'en in charge.
The princess sweetest perfumes did exhale.
Her manners were most gracious and polite
As of a well-born person. Every sort
Of gem and jewel sparkled from her robes.
She wore a ring—'twas *astokouna* called—
And yet another one, *glangkano* named,
And still another, with bright stones all carved
In fashion of Ceylon. Her tresses curled
Like to a full-blown flower, and on them shone
Full many precious stones. The *tourie* buds
Became her well. Her features were as bright
As those of some celestial being pure.
Fair Mendoudari thus was clad, and led
To the bride's seat, and at her either hand
Stood *mantris'* daughters seven with waving fans.
Meanwhile the *mangkouboumi* patiently
Achieved the tiring of the prince. He wore
A royal crown, made in the island fair
Called Nousa Antara, and a rich coat
Which opened at the sides, made in the West.
A chiselled necklace hung about his neck.
His tunic flamed with orange, like the robe
Of great Schahid Schah Pri. His girdle bright
Was cloth of *tjindi*, fringed with agates rare.
An amulet he wore with diamond pure,
With sacred words engraved of the Koran.
He wore a jewel like a butterfly,
Most beautiful, and many rings and gems.
His features of the rarest beauty were,
Like those of some divinity of heaven.
When thus arrayed, the youthful prince came forth
And made obeisance to his parents both.

He went to the appointed place, and all
The children of the court assembled there
Before him, while two sons of heralds stood
Beside him, waving fans like floating clouds.
All kept the strictest silence. Then a band
Of soldiers came, with blades all glittering.
The royal sword, all diamond decked, flashed rays
Of light. Three times around the island went
They all, with sound of music and the noise
Of bells. And all who heard in vain essayed
To estimate the number. Everyone
Ran forth to see the progress—men and women.
Some tore their garments, some their children lost,
Distracted by the pleasure and the noise.
When ended the procession, the young prince
At Princess Mendoudari's right was placed,
Within the palace. Then to them was brought
Rice called *adapadap*, and they became
A wedded pair. And all the folk dispersed.
In three days' time was Mendoudari dressed
Anew by Bidasari. She was robed
With vesture of embroidered silk. The prince
Was likewise gayly clad, to suit the glad
Occasion. Now again they made, in state,
A royal progress round about the isle.
The King and Bidasari rode in one
Grand chariot, and, within another, went
The prince and Mendoudari, his fair bride.
Then back they came for rest, upon the soft
Rich palace cushions. Then the mighty King
Of Kembajat inquired of his dear wife:
"What think'st thou, love? Shall we to-morrow morn
Return?" With smiles the Queen replied, "I bear
Thine orders on my head." Next day the hearts
Of all the royal company were filled
With joy. The officers assembled then
To take the King's commands, and he was pleased
To see them dutiful. The following morn
The song of the *bajans* awaked the King.
At early dawn each princess with her lord,

And all the officers, embarked upon
The ship. They sailed far from the island fair,
Nousa Antara, and in three days came
To Indrapura and the river's mouth.
When at the palace they arrived again,
The *mantris* came in joy and kissed their hands.
The King of Kembajat said that he wished
To go. Scarce had fair Indrapura's King
Heard that his parents to their home desired
At once to go, when he the *mantris* called
And orders gave. The King of Kembajat
Set out with his dear wife next day at dawn.
Within the palace of their daughter sweet
They met fair Indrapura's King. The King
Of Kembajat sat at his side, and said
In softest tones: "Well, Bidasari, child,
Thy parents now will homeward fare. Obey
The King, thy gracious husband, in all things.
The former merchant brought thee up. He will
A father be to thee. Strive hard to win
Thy husband's heart, and never disregard
His wishes." Scarcely had she heard these words
Than at her father's knees she fell, and shed
A flood of tears. The King embraced his child
And, weeping, said: "My daughter dear, pure gold,
My crown's chief gem, light of my very eyes,
Branch of my heart, be not disturbed, my soul,
Nor let thy heart be sad." The royal four
All wept together. Then the father said:
"My son, accomplished prince, we trust to thee
Our Bidasari. Show her the right path
If she aside should step, for hither she
As prisoner came. Correction should she need,
For us it will not be a shame." At this
Fair Indrapura's King was greatly moved.
He bowed and said: "My father, speak not thus.
I have the best opinion of the girl.
Our hearts are one, as body with the soul.
This kingdom all is hers, the guardian I
Of her possessions, and I'll satisfy

Her every wish." The King with joy replied:
" Well, daughter, jewel of my crown, thou art
No more beneath my sway, but wholly now
Under the orders of thy husband dear."
He much was moved, and to the *mangkouboumi*
Said, " Brother, take my treasures all, for we
Can never all thy goodness recompense."
The former merchant and his wife bowed low:
" Your gratitude, O prince, is great, but all
Thy treasures are thy royal daughter's meed.
For her we'll guard them." But the King replied:
" Nay, speak not thus, my brother. Should I give
All Indrapura's weight in purest gold
It would not pay thee for thy care and love.
We are to thee devoted from our hearts."
At dawn they breakfasted, but all were sad,
Because from Bidasari now must part
Her parents dear and brother. Much she wept
Because she felt her heart go out to him
Her brother. Then she said: " I've one to take
The place of parents, but where shall I find
A brother?" Princess Mendoudari bowed
To Bidasari, and they kissed with tears.
Fair Bidasari said: " My sister dear,
Sweet Mendoudari, when wilt thou return?
Stay not too long at Kembajat, for I
Could not thine absence bear. Farewell, my love."
The King embraced his daughter. Bitterly
Both wept. The royal father said, " Stay here,
My son-in-law, with thy dear wife." The King
Before his parents bowed. The youthful prince
Before the King his brother bowed, and went
To Bidasari's side, his sister dear,
With heavy heart. Then, weeping much, he said:
" O sister mine, gem of my crown, be not
So sorrowful. I go, but if thou dost
Desire, I'll come each year to visit thee."
Sweet Bidasari kissed him. But her grief
Was inexpressible. " O brother dear,
Illustrious prince," she said, " thine absence would

E'en then be much too long." The prince replied,
With bows: "Assuage thy grief, my sister dear.
For if the King permits, perhaps I may
Come sooner back to thee."
                          The mighty King
Of Indrapura said, in friendly tones:
"Although he be thy brother, still, my dear,
I love him much. We ne'er have had the least
Misunderstanding. Why art thou not gay?
And why art thou not willing he should go?
If 'twere not for thy father I would keep
Him here."
                The King departed, followed by
His son, who took his father just beyond
The gates. The *mangkouboumi* bowed his head
Before the King, who with much ardor said,
"O father of dear Bidasari, give
Aid and protection to thy lovely child."
The *mangkouboumi* bowed again, and said:
"Whate'er is fit, I'll do. Upon my head
I bear thine orders. I thy servant am."
The prince embraced the former merchant too,
And said, "O uncle dear, my sister guide,
And counsel her if any fault she doth."
Then said the King of Kembajat, "My son,
Come, let us start at once."
                            So forth he fared.
The prince and all the escort with him went.
A few days passed and they were home again.
New garments to the escort all were given,
And many presents to the officers.
By *mantris* four the King rich treasures sent
Unto his children loved, with many steeds
And elephants. When safely they arrived
At Indrapura, they appeared before
The *mangkouboumi*. He presented them
Unto the King, and said: "O sire, these gifts
Are from thy son." The King replied: "Why dost
Thou bring them here, my uncle? Keep them all
In thine own treasury." Then he retired

Within and said to Bidasari sweet:
" Thy father, dear, hath sent us presents rare,
And four young *mantris*, and a thousand men
With elephants and horses.   All is thine."
The fair young Queen with smiles to him replied:
" All that with me to share thou dost desire.
Whatever be thy wish, I wish it too."
The King adored his wife, and was to her
Devoted.   His great happiness increased
And his domains extended every year.
When Bidasari's royal birth was known,
The news spread far and wide, and everywhere
Was told.   The realm of Indrapura grew
More populous and powerful year by year.

The wicked Princess Lila Sari lived
Alone and desolate, in sadness deep
And full repentance for her evil deeds.

This song is weak because my skill is small.
My heart was deeply stirred.   And that is why
I made, poor fakir I, this poem here.
I have not made it long, because too sad
I was, and troubled.   Now at last 'tis done.
For this, at least, your blessings I deserve.

THE END.

SEDJARET MALAYOU

LEGENDS OF THE MALAY ARCHIPELAGO

—

[*Translated by M. Devic and Chauncey C. Starkweather*]

SEDJARET MALAYOU

ONCE upon a time lived King Iskender, son of King Darab. He traced his origin to Roum; Macedonia was his native country, and Dhoul-Garnein his surname. Now it happened that this prince set out upon his travels to find the place where the sun rose; and he arrived at the frontier of India. There reigned in this country a very powerful king, to whom half of India was in subjection; and his name was King Kida Hindi. As soon as King Kida Hindi heard of King Iskender's approach, he gave orders to his prime minister, who gathered together the armies and princes who were subject to him. When all were met together, he marched forth to meet King Iskender. The two armies engaged and the conflict was carried on with extreme activity on both sides, as is related in the history of King Iskender. Kida Hindi was defeated and taken alive. Iskender ordered him to embrace the true faith, and Kida Hindi embraced the faith and became enrolled in the religion of the prophet Abraham, the friend of God, to whom be the glory! Then King Iskender caused him to be clothed in a garment like his own, and bade him return to his own country.

King Kida Hindi was the father of a very beautiful girl, whose equal was not to be found in her day. Her face had the dazzling lustre of the sun or the moon; she was modest and discreet. Her name was Chehr-el-Beria. King Kida Hindi took his prime minister aside and said to him:

" I have summoned you to ask your advice on the subject of my daughter, whose equal in these days cannot be found. I have formed the project of presenting her to King Iskender."

The minister answered: " Your Majesty has made a wise decision."

" Very well," replied the King, " to-morrow, God willing, you shall go and find the prophet Khidar and relate to him the whole matter."

Next day accordingly the minister set out to find the prophet Khidar. After his departure King Kida Hindi commanded that the name of King Iskender should be inscribed on the coins and standards of his realm. When the minister approached the prophet Khidar he made a salaam to him, which the prophet returned and asked him to be seated. Then the minister spoke as follows:

"You must know, O prophet of God, that my King entertains for King Iskender an affection so fervent that I cannot describe it. He is the father of a girl who has no equal among the children of this world's monarchs from the rising to the setting sun. She is without a rival in face, wit, and goodness of disposition. Now the desire of the King is to present the princess before King Iskender, with the view of ultimately giving her to him for his wife."

Now the soldiers of King Souran laid siege against the walled town of Gangga-Chah Djouhan; but those on guard repulsed them, so that they could not get near. Seeing this, King Souran advanced, mounted on an untamed elephant. Taking no heed to the arrows that were launched against him by the defenders of the wall, he reached the gate and struck it with his mace. The gate gave way and King Souran entered, followed by his warriors.

When King Gangga-Chah Djouhan saw King Souran approaching, he seized his bow and shot an arrow with haste. The arrow struck the forehead of King Souran's elephant. The elephant fell on his knees. King Souran quickly leaped to the ground, drawing his sword as he did so; at a single stroke he struck through the neck of King Gangga-Chah, and the severed head rolled to the ground. The forces of Gangga-Nagara, as soon as they saw their prince fall, demanded the *aman* (*i.e.*, truce).

King Gangga-Chah Djouhan had a sister, named Princess Zaras Gangga. She was exceedingly beautiful. The victorious prince took her for his wife. Then he resumed his march.

Some time afterward he reached the city of Ganggayon. It was formerly a great city, the black stones of whose fortress survive even to this day. This fortress is at the extremity of the river Djoher. The name Ganggayon in the Siamese tongue means "treasury of emeralds." The King of the city was

Rajah Tchoulin; he was a powerful prince, to whom all the kings of the land did obeisance.

On the news of King Souran's approach, King Tchoulin called together all his troops and sent word to the kings who were his tributaries. When all were assembled he set out to repel the invaders. The multitude of his soldiers was like the waves of the sea; his elephants and horses stood up among them like islands; his flags and standards presented the appearance of a forest, and the cows' tails fluttering at the pike-heads presented the appearance of *lalang* ploughers.

The army came in four bodies and reached the banks of a river. There they saw the soldiers of King Souran, ranged like forest-trees. The Siamese exclaimed, "Pangkal," a word which means "river," and hence that river became known as the river Pangkal.

The soldiers of Siam at once joined battle with the soldiers of Kling, who were Hindoos; and the battle raged with indescribable confusion. The soldiers mounted on elephants pressed forward these great beasts; the men on horseback made their horses champ with fury; the lancers pressed home their lances; those who carried pikes plied them furiously; and those who bore sabres dealt many a doughty stroke. Blood flowed like rain. The crash of thunder would have been drowned by the shouts of the warriors and the clash of arms. The dust that rose from the plain obscured the brightness of the day like an eclipse of the sun. So complete was the confusion with which the contestants mingled that it was not possible to distinguish the combatants of either side: each assailant was at the same time the assailed, and he who struck with his weapon himself at the same moment was stricken with a blow. Sometimes the soldiers attacked a comrade by mistake. Every moment crowds of people on either side were killed and wounded, many horses and elephants had their throats cut, and the blood shed covered the ground. The dust had disappeared; the combatants were seen struggling in masses so compact that neither party was able to retire from the battle.

King Tchoulin managed to force a way by means of the elephant he rode through the innumerable horde of King Souran's soldiers; the corpses were piled up beneath his feet. A crowd of Hindoo warriors lost their lives. The rest of them began to give way. King Souran, on perceiving this, dashed forward to meet King Tchoulin in single combat. He mounted an untamed elephant eight cubits high that had no driver. But the elephant of King Tchoulin was also very brave. The two animals met; they attacked each other; the clash of their encounter was like the thunder that rends the earth; their tusks clashing and intertwining made a sound like that of a storm that never ceases. Neither could triumph over the other.

Then King Tchoulin raised himself upon the beast he rode and brandished a javelin. He hurled it against King Souran; the javelin struck the elephant on his flank and pierced deep. At the same time King Souran shot an arrow which smote King Tchoulin in the breast and came out at his back. That prince fell to the earth and expired. The soldiers seeing their king dead, broke ranks and took flight in utter disorder, pursued by the Hindoos, who put to the sword all they overtook. Penetrating the ramparts of Ganggayon the Hindoo soldiers pillaged the town; the booty was immense.

King Tchoulin had a daughter, extremely beautiful. Her name was the princess Ouangkion; she was presented to King Souran, who took her for his wife.

The King then resumed his march and arrived at Temasik. The rumor of his approach soon reached China. People said, " Lo! King Souran comes with a countless army to conquer China. He has already reached Temasik." This news was heard with dire alarm by the King of China. He said to his ministers and to his officers:

" What must be done to repel this invading multitude? If the King of Kling arrives here, he will doubtless ruin our country."

The prime minister said: " O King of the world; I have a device for repelling him."

" Very good," said the King; " do not fail to try it."

The prime minister therefore caused a *pilo*, or ship, to be fitted out with rusty needles. They took also two kinds of trees, kamses and jujube trees, laden with fruit; these were placed on board ship with the soil in which they grew. Old men who had lost their teeth were chosen for passengers and crew. To these the minister gave his instructions and they started for Temasik.

When they had reached this place King Souran was informed that a ship had arrived from China. " Go and ask these strangers," he said to his attendants, " at what distance does this country lie from us." The attendant put this question to the crew of the *pilo* and received the following reply:

" When we left China we were all still young, being scarcely twelve years old; and these trees were seeds which we had sown. But you see how old we are now, and how our teeth are fallen out; the grains of seed have become trees in fruit, and all this has happened during the time it has taken us to reach here."

At the same time they took the needles of which they had a large quantity and said as they showed them to the Hindoos:

" When we started from China, these were as thick as a man's arm, and now see how they are worn out by the rust. This will give you an idea of the length of the voyage: we could not keep count of the years and the months."

On hearing this answer of the Chinese, the Hindoos ran to report it to King Souran, to whom they repeated all they had heard.

" If the thing is as they say," replied the prince, " the land of China is still a very long way off. When shall we arrive there? We had better return home."

" His Majesty is undoubtedly right," said the officers.

King Souran meditated thus: " Behold, the contents of the land is known to me, but how can I learn the contents of the sea? I must needs enter the sea, in order to know it."

Then he summoned his engineers and skilful men, and ordered them to fashion a box of glass with lock and fastenings within, in order that he might shut himself in it. The engineers made the box of glass just as the King desired it; they furnished it with a chain of the purest gold; then they presented it to King Souran, who was exceedingly well pleased with it, and rewarded them all with rich presents.

The prince entered into the box, disappeared from the eyes of all present, and shut the door upon himself. They took the box to the sea, and let it descend even to the bottom. What treasures, what wealth, works of the Almighty, were seen by King Souran! The box fell until it reached a land called Dika. There King Souran came out of the box, and went forward, seeing most wonderful things. He arrived at a great and strongly fortified town, which he entered and saw a vast population, whose number God alone knows. This people, who call themselves the Badsam people, were composed of believers and unbelievers.

The inhabitants of the town were astonished to see the face of King Souran, and his garments they looked upon with astonishment. They conducted him to the presence of their King, whom they call Agtab-al-Ard (*i.e.,* Bowels of the Earth). This prince asked, "What man is this?"

"My lord," was the reply, "it is a stranger, who arrived a moment ago."

"Whence does he come?"

"We do not know."

Then the King addressed King Souran himself and said, "Who are you, and whence do you come?"

King Souran replied: "I come from the world; I am the king of men; my name is King Souran."

King Agtab-al-Ard was very much astonished on hearing these words. "There is, then," he said, "another world beside ours?"

"The world," replied King Souran, "contains many races."

"Glory to God almighty," said the King, full of surprise. Then he made King Souran ascend and sit with him on the royal throne.

Agtab-al-Ard had a daughter, of great beauty, named Princess Mah-tab-al-Bahri ("Moon of the Sea"). He gave her in marriage to King Souran. That prince dwelt three years with her and had three male children by her. When he thought about these three children King Souran felt much troubled. He said to himself: "What will become of them, here, under the earth? Or how shall I withdraw them hence?"

He went to see Agtab-al-Ard, and said to him: "If my sons grow up, will your Majesty allow me to see that they are brought into the upper world, in order that the royal line of Sultan Iskender Dhoul-Quameen may not be broken to the end of time?"

The King answered, "I shall not hinder you."

Then King Souran took leave of the King and prepared for his return. The King and his daughter shed many tears at parting. Then the King gave orders to bring the horse Sembrani, named Paras-al-Bahri ("Sea-horse"), which he gave to King Souran. The prince mounted the horse, which bore him from the sea, and carried him in the air above the billows.

The troops of King Souran caught sight of the horse Sembrani, and recognized in its rider their King. The prime minister at once took a beautiful mare and led it to the shore. The sea-horse saw the mare and came to land to meet her, and King Souran descended. Then the horse Sembrani went back into the sea.

King Souran said to his wise men and engineers: " Raise a monument which shall witness to my journey in the sea; for I wish the memory of it to be preserved even to the Resurrection day. Write out the story, so that it may be told to all my descendants."

In obedience to the words of the King the wise men and engineers set up a stone on which they traced an inscription in the tongue of Hindostan. This done, King Souran gathered a quantity of gold, silver, jewels, gems, and precious treasures, which he laid up under the stone.

" At the end of the centuries," he said, " there will come a king among my descendants who will find these riches. And this king will subdue every country over which the wind blows."

After this, King Souran returned to the land of Kling. There he built a mighty city, protected by a wall of black stone having seven rows of masonry thick and nine fathoms high; the engineers made it with such skill that the joints of the stones were invisible, and the wall seemed cast of a single substance. The gate was of steel, enriched with gold and precious stones.

This rampart enclosed seven hills. In the centre of the city extended a pool vast as the sea; from one bank it was impossible to discern an elephant standing up on the other. It contained very many kinds of fishes. In the midst of it rose a very lofty island, always covered with a mantle of mist. The King caused to be planted there every sort of flowering and fruit-bearing tree to be found in the world. None was lacking, and to this island the King would repair when he wished for recreation.

He caused also to be planted on the banks of the pool a vast forest wherein wild animals were at large. And when the King wished to hunt, or catch elephants in the snare, he went to this forest. When the town was completed the King called it after himself, Souran-Bidgi-Nagara, and this town still exists in the province of Kling.

In short, if one wished to relate all the rest of King Souran's history he would find it as long as that of Sidi Hanza.

The Adventures of Badang

It is related that there once lived at Salouang a husbandman who owned a slave named Badang, whom he employed in clearing forest-land. It happened one day that Badang spread his nets in the river; but on the following morning he found his net quite empty, and by its side some fish-scales and fish-bones. The same thing took place for some days following. Badang flung the fish-scales (*sisik*) into the river; from which circumstance was derived the river's name, Besisik.

Meanwhile the slave said to himself: "Who is it who eats the fish caught in my net? I must watch and find out."

With this intention he hid one day behind some trees and saw a *hantou*, or evil genius, or monster, who was eating the fish taken in his net. This *hantou* had eyes red as fire, his hair was like woven osiers, and his beard fell down to his waist. Badang drew his knife, and, screwing up his courage, rushed up to the *hantou* and seized him.

"Every day," he said, "you eat up my fish. But this time you shall die at my hands."

On hearing these words, the *hantou* was afraid, and slipped aside, wishing to avoid the hands of his adversary; but failing to do so, he said to him: "Do not kill me; I will give you what you wish, on condition that you spare my life."

Badang thought: "If I ask for riches, my master will claim them. If I ask the power to become invisible, they will put me to death as a sorcerer. Therefore it is best for me to ask for the gift of physical strength, in order that I may do the work of my master."

In accordance with this resolution, Badang said to the *hantou*, "Give me the gift of physical strength; let me be strong enough to tear down and to uproot the trees; that is, that I may tear down, with one hand, great trees, a fathom or two in girth."

The *hantou* answered: "Your prayer is granted. You wish for strength; I will give it to you; but first it is necessary that you eat up what I vomit."

"Very well," said Badang; "vomit, and I will eat it up." The *hantou* vomited, and Badang set to work to eat it. He held the *hantou* by the beard, and would not let him go. Then he attempted the uprooting of great trees; and, seeing that he tore them up with ease, he let go the beard of the *hantou.*

Afterward, coming and going through the forest, he tore down enormous trees; he carried off, roots and all, those of a fathom or two in girth. As for the small ones, he tore them up by handfuls and flung them on all sides. In a moment the forest which had been a wilderness became level as a great plain.

When his master saw this work he said: "Who has cleared our land? For I see that it is suddenly freed entirely from trees and brushwood."

"It is I," said Badang, "who have effected this clearance."

Then answered the master: "How have you been able to do this, single-handed, so quickly and in one job?"

Then Badang related all the details of his adventure, and his master gave him his liberty.

The report of these occurrences reached Singapore. King Krama immediately ordered that Badang be brought before him, and he called him Raden (*i.e.,* Royal Prince).

Once upon a time the King of Singapore ordered Badang to fetch for his repast the fruit of *kouras*, at the river Sayang. Badang went there alone in his *pilang,* or boat, which was eight fathoms long, and he punted it with a pole cut from the trunk of a kampas-tree a fathom in girth.

When he arrived at the river Sayang, he clasped the *kouras*-tree. The branches broke, the tree fell, and his head struck against a huge rock. His head was not injured, but the rock was split in two. This stone is still seen to-day on the river Sayang, and it bears the name of Balou-blah, which means the "Riven Rock." His pole and boat have also been preserved to the present day. The day following his exploit Badang started back for Singapore, with his *pilang* completely laden with sugar-cane, bananas, and *keladion,* or edible lily, root. He had eaten the whole cargo before he arrived at Djohor-the-Old.

On another occasion the King of Singapore had caused a large ship to be built, fifteen fathoms long, in front of the palace. The vessel being finished, between forty and fifty men were ordered to push it into the water. They were unable to launch it. As many as 2,000 or 3,000 persons were equally unsuccessful. Then the King ordered Badang to undertake the operation. Badang undertook the task unaided, and pushed with such force that the vessel went right across the strait to the other shore. For this feat the King appointed him *houloubalong,* or officer of military rank.

A report reached the province of Kling that among the officers of the King was a man of extraordinary strength, named Badang. Now there was a powerful athlete at the court of the King of Kling, who had no rival in the country. His name was Madia-Bibjaya-Pelkrama. The King ordered him to go to Singapore with seven vessels; " Go," said he, " and wrestle with this officer. If he defeat you, give him as a prize the cargo of the seven vessels; if you are victorious, demand of him an equal forfeit."

" I obey, your Majesty," said the athlete, and started off with the seven vessels.

When he arrived at Singapore they brought news to the King of the city, saying: " An athlete has arrived from the land of Kling to compete with Badang in many kinds of sports. If he is defeated, he will leave the cargo of his seven vessels as forfeit."

The King came out of his palace to give audience. The Hindoo athlete presented himself. The prince told him to try a bout with Badang. Badang beat him in every round.

Now facing the *balerong,* or court of audience, was an enormous rock. The athlete said to Badang: " Come, let us match our strength by lifting this stone. Whoever cannot lift it will be conquered."

" Do you try first," said Badang.

The athlete commenced, and made many attempts without succeeding in lifting it. At last, mustering all his strength, he raised it to the height of his knee and let it fall again.

" Now it is your turn, my master," he said.

" Very good," answered Badang, and lifting the stone he swung it in the air, then hurled it toward the river, at the entrance to the town, where it is still seen at the extremity of the point of Singapore.

The athlete of Kling, thus vanquished, handed to Badang the seven vessels and their cargoes; then he returned, very much saddened and mortified by his defeat.

Now the report came to the country of Perlak that there was at Singapore an officer of the King named Badang without a rival in extraordinary strength. The King of Perlak, so runs the story, had an athlete named Bandarang, also very strong and of a great reputation. This athlete was before the King when they spoke of Badang.

" My lord," he asked, " is Badang stronger than I am? If you will permit me, I will go to Singapore to try an assault with him."

" Very well; go to Singapore," said the King. Turning to the prime minister, Toun Parapatih, he said:

" Get ready a *praho*, for I am going to send Bandarang to Singapore." When all was ready, a royal litter was prepared and the minister embarked with the athlete, and after a while reached Singapore. Prince Sri Rana Ouira Krama received the King's litter in the audience-chamber, among the radjas, ministers, body-guards, heralds, and other grand officers upon his command.

Then the prince, addressing the ambassador, asked: " With what commission is our brother charged? "

The ambassador replied: " Behold, I have received the command of your illustrious younger brother to bring here this subject Bandarang, to try his strength with Badang. If Bandarang is vanquished, your brother will place at your Majesty's feet the contents of a storehouse; and if Badang succumbs, you shall offer us the equivalent."

" Very well," said the King; " to-morrow everything shall be arranged for the struggle." The King retired to the palace, summoned Badang, and said to him:

" You know, Badang, that to-morrow you will have to contend with Bandarang."

" My lord," answered Badang, " know that this man is a powerful athlete, of extraordinary strength, famous in all coun-

tries. If your slave is vanquished will it not cast some dis-
credit on the sovereign? If your Majesty thinks it wise, let
us both be called into your presence together, so that I may
test him; and if I feel myself capable of competing with him,
we will have the contest; but if he is too strong for me, then
your Majesty can oppose the struggle."

"You are right," said the King. That is why, when night
came, the prince invited Toun Parapatih Pendek, Bandarang,
and their companions. When they arrived they were served
with a collation. Bandarang was seated beside Badang, who
began to test him. They tried each other's strength without
attracting attention.

At the end of an hour, when the guests were in wine, the
King asked Badang if he were strong enough to struggle with
Bandarang, who declared that he was equal to him. On the
other hand, when Toun Parapatih Pendek had returned to the
ship, Bandarang said to him:

"Lord, if you will permit me to advise, there will be no contest between Badang and me. I might not conquer, for I have
learned how powerful he is."

"Very well," said the minister; "it is very easy to arrange
that."

So the minister said to the King: "It is my opinion that
we should prevent this struggle; for if one of the contestants
should be vanquished in some bad way, a quarrel might arise
out of it between your Majesty and the sovereign your brother."

The King agreed, and the ambassador asked leave to return
home. The prince had a letter written for the King of Perlak.
It was carried in state on board the ship and the envoy, after
receiving vestments of honor, set sail to his own country. Arriving, he told the King all that had taken place. Later Badang
died and was buried at Bourou. When the news of his death
arrived at that country, the King of Kling sent a carved stone,
which is now seen at Bourou.

And now as to the kings of Pasey. The authors of this story
declare that there were two brothers named Marah who lived
near Pasangan. They were originally from the mountain of
Sanggong. The elder was named Mara-Tchaga, and the
younger Marah-Silou. Marah-Silou was engaged in casting
nets. Having taken some *kalang-kalang*, he rejected them

and cast his net anew. The *kalang-kalang* were caught again. After several attempts with the same result, Marah-Silou had these *kalang-kalang* boiled. And behold, the wretched things became gold and their froth became silver. Marah-Silou caught more *kalang-kalang*, boiled them, and again saw them become gold and silver. He had thus acquired much store of gold and silver, when one day the news came to Marah-Tchaga that his younger brother was catching *kalang-kalang*, and he was so irritated that he wished to kill him. When Marah-Silou learned of this design, he took refuge in the forest of Djawn. The place where he fished is still called the Plain of Kalang-Kalang.

Marah-Silou, established in the forest of Djawn, gave gold to those who dwelt there, and they all obeyed his commands. One day when he was hunting, his dog, named Si Pasey, began to bark on a slight hill which one would have believed made by the hand of man. Climbing the small hill he saw an ant as big as a cat. He took it and ate it up. The place was afterward called Samodra; that is to say, " The Big Ant." Now it is said that the prophet of God—blessings be upon him!—once told his companions:

" There will be a country some day, toward the south, called Samoudra. When you hear it spoken of, hasten thither to convert the inhabitants to Islam, for in that country many will become the friends of God. But there will also be the king of a country called Mataba, whom you must take with you."

A long time after this decree of the prophet, the fakir Mahomet went to Samoudra. Reaching the shore, he met Marah-Silou, who was gathering shells. The fakir asked him:

" What is the name of this country? "

" Its name is Samoudra," answered Marah-Silou.

" And what is the sovereign's name? "

" I am the sovereign of all who dwell here," said Marah-Silou.

The fakir Mahomet converted Marah-Silou to Islam and taught him the words of the creed. Now Marah-Silou being asleep dreamed that he was in the presence of the prophet of God, and the prophet said to him, " Marah-Silou, open your mouth." He opened it and the prophet spat in it, and Marah-

Silou, awaking, perceived throughout his whole body a perfume like that of spikenard. When day broke he told his dream.

"This is truly the country of Samoudra of which the prophet of God has spoken," said the fakir Mahomet. Bringing from the ship all the royal ensigns aboard, he proclaimed Marah-Silou king with the title of Sultan Melik-es-Salih.

Sultan Melik-es-Salih sent Sidi Ali Ghaiath-ed-Din to the country of Perlak. This prince had three daughters, two of blood-royal on their mother's side, and one born of a concubine. The latter was called the princess Ganggang. When Sidi Ali Ghaiath arrived at Perlak they showed him the three daughters. The two sisters of the blood-royal were seated lower than the princess Ganggang, who occupied a high seat. The latter, by order of her father, was cleaning arec nuts for her two sisters, like one doing the honors of the household. She wore rose-colored garments and a violet cloak. Her ears were adorned with *soubangs* made with the young leaves of the *lontar*. She was very beautiful.

Sidi Ali Ghaiath-ed-Din said to the King of Perlak, "That one of your daughters who is seated above is the one I ask in marriage for my master, your son." The envoy knew not that Princess Ganggang was the daughter of a concubine.

The King burst out laughing. "Very well," he said, "let the will of my son be accomplished." Then he gave orders to equip 100 *prahos*, and Toun Parapatih received the command to accompany the princess to the country of Samoudra.

Sultan Melik-es-Salih went to meet the princess as far as Djambou Ayer. He introduced her into Samoudra with a thousand honors and splendors, and married her. The marriage accomplished, the prince gave presents to the ministers and to the officers, and showed himself lavish in gold and silver to the poor of the country. As for Toun Parapatih Pendek, he took leave to return to Perlak. Sultan Melik-es-Salih and the princess Ganggang had two sons who received from the prince the names of Sultan Melik-ed-Dhahir and Sultan Melik-el-Mansour. The elder was confided to Sidi Ali Ghaiath-ed-Din and the other to Sidi Ali Asmai-ed-Din. Years passed and the two young princes had grown up. Perlak had been conquered by an enemy come from the opposite coast, and the inhabitants of the country had migrated to Samoudra. Sultan Melik-es-Salih conceived the plan of founding a city to establish his sons there. He said to the great ones, "To-morrow I shall go hunting." The next morning he set out, mounted on an elephant called Perma Diouana. He passed to the other side of the water. When he came to land his dog Si Pasey began to bark. The prince ran up and saw that he was barking before a hillock, sufficiently extended for the erection of a palace and its dependencies, level on top and well disposed. Sultan Melik had the ground cleared and built a palace and a city there. After the name of his dog he called the palace Pasey, and established as king his son Sultan Melik-ed-Dhahir, with Sidi Ali Ghaiath as minister. He divided his men, his elephants, and his royal standards into two parts, one for each of his sons.

Some time after this, the prince, having fallen ill, commanded the grandees to assemble and called his two sons and spoke as follows: "Oh, my two sons, and you all, my companions, my last hour is approaching. You men be good to those whom I leave behind. And you, my sons, beware of being envious of another's good, and of the wives and daughters of your subjects. Maintain between you the union of two brothers, abstain from all injustice, and avoid between you every cause of quarrel." He said also to Sidi Ali Gaiath-ed-Din and to Sidi Asmai-ed-Din:

"Oh, my brothers, take care of these two sons. Stir not up trouble between them. Be faithful to them and never give your allegiance to another king." The two young princes bowed their heads and wept.

As for the two ministers, "Lord," they said, "light of our eyes, we swear by the sovereign Master who created the worlds that we will never break our promises, that we will never lack in our fidelity or render homage to another king than your two well-beloved sons."

Then Sultan Melik-es-Salih named his son Melik-el-Mansour, King of Samoudra. Three days later he died and was buried in the interior of the palace. Their father dead, the two young princes, his sons, commanded the royal herald to assemble the officers and soldiers, elephants and horses, as well as the royal insignia of the country of Pasey. And the two cities grew

and flourished more and more. God knows best the truth.
He is our aid and our refuge.

Now this is the story of the King Chehr-en-Naoui. His
power was great, his officers and soldiers innumerable. They
told this prince that the country of Samoudra had a large population, many merchants, and a powerful king. Chehr-en-Naoui
said to his officers:

"Which of you would be able to take the King of Samoudra?"

One of his officers very strong and brave, Aoui Ditchou,
bowed and said: "Lord, if your Majesty will give me 4,000
chosen warriors, I will take the King of Samoudra alive and
bring him to the foot of your Majesty's throne."

The King gave him the 4,000 warriors and 100 ships. When
they were ready Aoui Ditchou sailed toward Samoudra, feign-
ing that the ships were bent on commerce up to the very moment when they reached the end of the voyage. Then he caused
it to be said that he was an ambassador of the King Chehr-en-
Naoui, and the King of Samoudra sent some officers to receive
him.

Landing, Aoui Ditchou put into four chests four lusty *houlou-
balongs*, to whom he said: "Presently, when you are in the
presence of the King of Samoudra, open the chests, leap out,
and seize the King." The chests were fastened from within.
They took them ashore in state as presents from the King
Chehr-en-Naoui. When they were in the presence of the
prince, a message couched in flattering terms was read, and
the chests were brought in. Immediately the *houlou-balongs*
opened the chests, sprang out, and seized the sovereign. The
soldiers uttered fierce cries and unsheathed their arms to attack
the band of Chehr-en-Naoui's men. But the latter cried:

"If you fall upon us, we will kill your King."

So the soldiers paused in their attack. Aoui Ditchou and
his people returned, bringing with them the King of Samoudra.
They crossed the sea and regained their own country. There
the prisoner-King was conducted by Aoui Ditchou before King
Chehr-en-Naoui, who was very joyful and loaded the head of
the expedition and all his companions with honors. As for the
King of Samoudra, they made him a poultry-keeper.

Now let us talk of Sidi Ali Gaiath-ed-Din. Having consulted with the principal ministers in the country of Samoudra, he equipped a ship and purchased a cargo of Arabic merchandise, for the inhabitants of Pasey at that time all knew the Arabic language. Sidi Ali and the soldiers whom he embarked on the ship with him took all the ways and manners of the Arabs. The minister being on board and all being made ready, they set sail for the country of Chehr-en-Naoui, where they arrived after a short voyage. Sidi Ali landed and went to present himself to the King, bearing as a gift a tree of gold, of which the fruits were all sorts of precious stones, and which was worth an almost inconceivable sum. When the prince saw this present he asked:

"What do you want of me?"

Sidi Ali replied, "We want nothing."

The King was highly pleased, although surprised by such a magnificent present. And he said to himself, "Now, what can be the aim of these people giving me all this?" The pretended Arabs returned to their ships. A few days after, the master of the ship returned to visit the King. This time he brought as a present a chess-board of gold of which the chessmen were of precious stones, which was worth an enormous sum.

"What do you want of me?" again asked the prince. "Speak, that I may satisfy you."

And they replied, "We ask for nothing."

Then they returned to the ship. Some time later, when the favorable monsoon blew for their return homeward, Sidi Ali Ghaiath thought upon his departure. He went to see the King, laden with a present which consisted of two golden ducks, male and female, enriched with precious stones, and in a big golden basin. He filled this golden basin with water, put in the ducks. They began to swim, dive, and pursue each other, a sight at which the King marvelled much.

"I beg of you to tell me," he said, "what you desire of me. By the God whom I worship, I swear to fulfil your wishes."

Then Sidi Ali answered: "Lord, if it is the accomplishment of your favor, we beg that you will give us your poultry-keeper."

"It is the King of Pasey that you ask of me. But, very well, I grant him to you."

"It is because he is a Mussulman," said the strangers, "that we ask him of your Majesty."

The King Chehr-en-Naoui delivered therefore the Sultan Melik-ed-Dhahir to Sidi Ali Gaiath-ed-Din, who took him on board the ship, gave him a bath, and then clothed him in royal raiment. The wind blew, they weighed anchor, set sail, and after a certain time arrived at the country of Samoudra. And God knows the truth. He is our aid and our refuge.

Now we are going to speak of the King Melik-el-Mansour at Samoudra. This prince said one day to Sidi Ali Asmai-ed-Din:

"I would like to go and see how my brother is getting along."

The minister answered, "Do not go, my lord, for fear of misfortune." And, indeed, he tried to restrain his master. The prince would listen to nothing, and finally the minister was silent. He ordered the drums to beat, in order to make the announcement, "Sultan Melik-el-Mansour is going to see the country of his brother."

Sidi Ali Asmai-ed-Din was not satisfied. He was an old minister who knew that out of every affair causes of trouble may arise. But it was his duty to obey. The prince started. He made the tour of the city of Pasey, and then entered the palace of the Sultan Melik-ed-Dhahir. There he fell in love with one of the ladies-of-honor of his brother's court, and a quarrel arose between the two brothers on her account. Sultan Melik-ed-Dhahir felt in the bottom of his heart a violent irritation toward his brother.

Now he had a son named Radja Ahmed, very young when his father was captured, but grown up when the prince was restored from the hands of Chehr-en-Naoui. Sidi Ali Ghaiath-ed-Din having withdrawn from affairs, a minister named Para-patih Toulous Toukang Sikari had replaced him in his ministerial functions. One day the King said to the minister:

"What is your opinion concerning the act of Sultan Melik-el-Mansour?"

The minister answered: "We have a means——"

"But," answered the King, "it might involve his death."

"If he dies," replied the minister, "my name shall be no longer Toukang."

"Give a family fête for your son Sultan Ahmed. We will invite Sultan Melik-el-Mansour to the festival."

Sultan Melik-ed-Dhahir gave orders then to decorate the city and made preparations for the fête, and sent to find Sultan Melik-el-Mansour. This prince was with Sidi Ali Asmai-ed-Din and his officers. They introduced the prince and his minister, but left the officers outside. When they had entered, Sultan Melik-ed-Dhahir caused them both to be seized and ordered one of his officers to conduct his brother to Mandjang. "As for you," he said to Sidi Ali, "stay here. Do not try to go with your master or I'll cut off your head."

Sidi Ali answered: "Rather let my head be separated from my body than that the servant should be separated from his master."

So the King had his head cut off. The head was thrown into the sea and the body impaled at the entrance to the Bay of Pasey. While they were taking the Sultan Melik-el-Mansour toward the east in a *prabo*, at the moment when they arrived near Djambou Ayer, the pilot saw a human head floating in the water near the rudder. He recognized the head of Sidi Ali. Informed of this event, Sultan Melik-el-Mansour caused the head to be taken from the water. It was indeed that of his minister. Casting his glances toward the land: "Behold," he said, "the Plain of Illusions." And it bears that name, "Padang-Maya," to this day. The prince sent to his brother and demanded the body of Sidi Ali; joined the head with the body, and buried both in the Plain of Illusion. Then he went back to Mandjang.

After the departure of the Sultan Melik-el-Mansour, King Melik-ed-Dhahir had the family festival. The Sultan Melik-el-Mansour had been at Mandjang three years when the Sultan Melik-ed-Dhahir bethought him of his brother.

"Alas," he said, "I was truly too unwise. For a woman my brother dethroned, and his minister is dead."

And the prince repented. He ordered some of his officers to go and find his brother at Mandjang. They therefore brought back Sultan Melik-el-Mansour with the regard due to a king. When they arrived near the Plain of Maya, the prince landed to visit the tomb of Sidi Ali Asmai-ed-Din. "I salute you, my father," he said. "Stay here, my father. As for me I go away, called by my brother."

From the interior of the tomb Sidi Ali answered: "Where would the prince go? It is better to remain here."

When the prince heard these words, he made his ablutions, said a couple of prayers, then stretched himself upon the tomb and expired. They bore to Sultan Melik-ed-Dhahir the news that his brother was dead, in the Plain of Maya, in the tomb of Sidi Ali Asmai-ed-Din. He started at once, went to the place, and had his brother, Sultan Melik-el-Mansour, buried with the ceremonies of great kings. Then, after returning to Pasey, a prey to grief, he abdicated the throne in favor of his son, Sultan Ahmed.

Some time after this, Sultan Melik-ed-Dhahir fell ill. He gave Sultan Ahmed his last instructions. " O my son," said he, " light of my eyes, treasure of my heart, never neglect the advice of your old servitors. In every affair take counsel with your ministers. Neglect not the duties of piety to God, the sovereign Master. Beware of injustice to men."

Sultan Ahmed heard in tears the last words of his father. The prince died, and they buried him near the mosque.

Sultan Ahmed was for many years on the throne and governed with much justice. Now, the author of this story says: "There was at Pasey a servant of God named Toun Djana Khatite. This man made the voyage to Singapore with two companions. Crossing the square of Singapore he passed by the palace of the King and saw the Queen. Near the palace was an areca tree, and while Toun Djana was looking at the Queen the tree split in two. At sight of this, King Sri Maharadja was extremely irritated. ' You see,' he cried, ' the conduct of Toun Djana Khatite. To call the attention of the Queen, he has acted thus. And he ordered him to be killed. So Toun Djana was led to the place of punishment, near a cake-shop, where Toun Djana Khatite received the blow of the poniard; his blood ran on the earth, but his body disappeared and no one could ever tell what became of it. The cake-shop-keeper covered the blood with the cake-cover, and the cake-cover was changed into stone, which is still seen at Singapore. According to a tradition, the body of Toun Djana Khatite was transported to Langkaoui and there buried."

Some time later came the sea-monsters called *toudaks* and attacked Singapore. They leaped upon the shore, and people

who were there died in great numbers, overtaken by these
toudaks. If they struck a man on the breast, they pierced to
his back. If they struck the neck or the loins, they pierced
clear through from one side to the other. There were many
killed. People ran about crying:

" The *toudaks* are attacking us ! "

" What shall we do ? "

" How many dead ? We shall all perish ! "

Padouka Sri Maharadja in great haste mounts the elephant
and goes forth, followed by his ministers, his body-guards, and
all his officers. Arriving at the seashore he sees with horror
the work of these monsters, the *toudaks*. Whoever was
wounded by them inevitably perished. The number of the
victims became larger and larger. The prince ordered the men
to make a rampart of their legs, but in their boundings the
toudaks succeeded in passing this barrier. They came like the
rain, and the slaughter was terrible. While this was happening
a young boy said :

" Why make thus a rampart of our legs? That is an artifice
very much to our hurt. If we should make a rampart of the
trunks of banana-trees, would not that be better ? "

When Padouka Sri Maharadja heard the words of the child,
" He is right," he said. And on his orders they hastened to
construct a barrier of banana-tree trunks. When the *toudaks*
came bounding along their snouts were buried in the tree-
trunks, and the men ran up and killed them. There perished
thus of these *toudaks* a number beyond computation. Their
bodies formed heaps on the shore, and all the population of
Singapore did not suffice to eat them. And the *toudaks* ceased
their leapings. They say, by the force of their boundings the
toudaks reached the elephant of the prince and tore the sleeve
of his cloak. About this they made a song:

> " The boundings of the *toudaks* tore
> The mantle which the Sultan wore,
> But here they ceased their onset wild,
> Thanks to the wisdom of a child."

While Padouka Sri Maharadja was returning, the grandees
said to him : " Lord, this child, though so young, has much
wit. What will it be when he has grown up? You had better

get rid of him." That is why they found it just that the King should give the order for him to be killed.

After they had caused this young boy to perish, it seems that the city of Singapore felt the weight of his blood.

Padouka Sri Maharadja reigned some time still and then died. He had as successor his son Padja Is Keuder Chah, who married the daughter of Toun Parapatih Toulous, and by her had a son named Radja Ahmed Timang-timanganga Radja Besar Mouda. This young prince was handsome and well formed, without equal in those days. When he was of age his father married him to the daughter of the King Sala-miam, King of Kota-Mahlikie, who was named Kamar-al-Adjaaib, a princess of unrivalled beauty. King Is Keuder Chah had a *bendahari*, or major-domo, named Lang Radjouna Tapa, of the race of ancient inhabitants of Singapore, father of a very beautiful girl in the court of the King. The other court ladies calumniated this young woman, and the King in a rage ordered her to be impaled in the corner of the market-place.

Lang Radjouna Tapa was extremely wounded by the treatment of his daughter. "If in truth my daughter had offended," said he, "you might have simply had her killed. But why dishonor us thus?" On this he wrote a letter to Java saying, "If the Batara of Madjapahit wishes to attack Singapore let him come at once, for I will give him entrance into the fortifications."

When the Batara of Madjapahit had read this letter he caused to be equipped 300 junks and a great quantity of other boats. A hundred thousand Javanese embarked, crossed the sea, and attacked Singapore. At the end of several days King Is Keuder commanded his major-domo to carry rice for the rations of the troops. Lang Radjouna Tapa answered, "There is no more, my Lord." For he wished to betray him. At daybreak he opened the gates of the fortifications and the Javanese entered. Inside the town there was a frantic combat. So many people were killed on each side that blood flowed like water. From this came the marks of blood which are seen to this day in the Plain of Singapore. The natives ceased their struggle and King Is Keuder escaped, descending from Salitar to the Moara coast. By the will of God, the house of

Lang Radjouna Tapa was overturned, the storehouse for rice fell to pieces, and the rice was changed to earth. The *bendahari* himself and his wife were changed to stone, and these stones are still found in the ditch at Singapore. After this victory the Javanese returned to Madjapahit.

On arriving at Moara, King Is Keuder halted at nightfall. Now there came a multitude of iguanas, and, when day dawned they saw them gathered in a crowd near the halting-place. They killed them and threw their bodies into the river. But at night, iguanas again came in mass. The next morning the Singaporeans killed them, but that night as many more arrived. So that the place became putrid from the multitude of their bodies. The quarter is still called Biaoak Bousok, or " Putrid Iguanas."

King Is Keuder Chah set out and came to another place, where he built a fort. But all they constructed by day was overturned by night. And the place still bears the name of Kota-Bourok, or " Ruined Fort."

Starting from there the King advanced into the interior during many days and came to the Saning Oudjong. He found this place agreeable and left a minister there. Hence comes it that to this day Saning Oudjong is the residence of a minister. Then the King returned toward the coast near a river at the shore of the sea. The river was called Bartain. Is Keuder Chah halted at the foot of a very bushy tree. Then he began hunting. His dog, chasing some game, was struck by the foot of a little white gazelle and fell into the water. On this the prince cried:

" Here is a good place to build a city, for even the little gazelles are valiant here."

And all the grandees said, " His Majesty is right." The King therefore gave orders for the construction of a city at this place. He asked, " What is the name of this tree against which I have been leaning? "

Someone answered, " It is a malaka-tree." " Very well," said he, " let Malaka be the name of the city."

The prince established himself at Malaka. He had lived thirty-two years at Singapore, up to the capture of that town by the Javanese. He lived for three years more at Malaka, and then died, by the vicissitudes of this world, and had as successor his son Radja Besar Mouda.

This prince governed with justice. He regulated the etiquette of the court. He first established a ministry of ceremonies to direct people who came to Balerong, and forty heralds who stood below the throne ready to take the orders of the King and carry to him the words of the public. He instituted among the sons of the grandees a body of pages serving as royal messengers and bearing everywhere the royal equipage.

This prince had three sons, Radeu Bagousa, Radeu Tengah, and Radeu Anoumah, who all married daughters of Bauhara Toun Parapatih Toulous. At his death, Radeu Bagousa took his functions with the title of Toun Parapatih Permouka Berdjadjar.

When, by the vicissitudes of the world, King Besar Mouda died, his son Radeu Tengah succeeded him. The latter had a son called Radja Kitchil Bessar, who at his death was his successor. He was just and guarded the interests of his subjects. No one in his time among the kings of the world equalled him in liberality. And the city of Malaka became large, well peopled, and the meeting-place of merchants. This King married a daughter of Toun Parapatih Permouka Berdjadjar, and by her had two sons, Radja Kitchil Mainbang and Radja Makat. He reigned for a certain time, when one night he dreamed that he was in the presence of the glorious prophet of God, on whom be blessings! And the prophet said to him, " Recite the words of the creed." And Radja Kitchil Bessar did as the prophet commanded.

" Your name shall be Sultan Mahomet," said the prophet. " To-morrow at the moment of the Asr (in the afternoon) there will arrive a ship from Djedda, from which the men will descend to pray on the shore of Malaka. Follow all their orders."

" Yes, Lord," replied the prince, " I shall obey your word."

And the prophet disappeared. When day came the King awaked. He perceived upon his body the odor of spikenard and saw that he bore certain marks. " It is clear," he thought, " that my dream does not come from Satan." And he began to recite without relaxation the words of the creed.

The ladies-of-honor who were in the palace were very much surprised to hear the King speak thus. " Has the King been touched by Satan, or has he lost his wits? Let us hasten to inform the *bendahari*." They ran to tell the *bendahari*, who came at once, entered the palace, and saw the King repeating without cessation the words of the creed.

" What is this language in which the King is speaking? " said the minister.

" Last night," said the King, " I dreamed that I was in the presence of the glorious prophet." And he told his dream to the *bendahari*.

" If your dream is not an illusion," said the latter, " what is the sign? "

" Here is the sign that proves that I have really seen in a dream the prophet of God. Furthermore, the prophet told me: ' To-day, at Asr, there will arrive a ship from Djedda, from which the people will descend to say their prayers on the shore of Malaka. Follow their directions.' "

The *bendahari* was surprised at seeing the marks on the King.

" Truly," he said, " if a ship arrives at the hour stated, then your dream is a reality. If it does not arrive, we shall judge that Satan must have troubled your spirit."

The King replied, " My father is right." And the *bendahari* returned to his house.

Now at the hour of Asr there arrived a ship from Djedda which cast anchor. The master came on shore. He was called Sidi Abd-el-Aziz. He said his prayers on the shore of Malaka. The inhabitants, astonished at the sight, said:

" Why does he stoop so and prostrate himself so? "

And to see him better, the people pressed around, leaving no spot vacant, and making a great tumult.

The noise reached the palace, and the King mounted an elephant and came in haste, accompanied by his grandees. He saw the master making all the ceremonies of his prayer, and all was in evident accord with the dream.

"It is exactly as in my dream," he exclaimed to the *bendahari* and the grandees.

When the master had finished praying, the King made his elephant stoop, and took up the master with him and carried him to the palace. The *bendahari* and the grandees all became Mussulmans, and by command of the King so did all the population, men and women, great and small, young and old.

The master taught the King the ceremonies of prayer, and
gave him the name of Sultan Mahomet Chah. The *bendahari*
received the title of Sri Ouak Radja; that is to say, " Paternal
Uncle of the King," which he was in fact. And that is the
first title of the *bendahari*.

Sultan Mahomet regulated the ceremonial customs of the
court. He was the first to prohibit yellow for the clothes of
the person strange to the court, for handkerchiefs, borders of
curtains, pillow-cases, mattresses, coverings of all kinds, ornaments of every nature, as well as for the decoration of houses.

Furthermore the use of only three kinds of garments was
permitted—the *kain*, the *badjoa*, and the *destar*. It was also
forbidden to construct houses with projections sustained upon
pillars not touching the ground, or with pillars extending beyond the roof or with observatories. The *prahos* could have no
windows in front. It was forbidden to carry clasps or ornaments of gold on the *kris*. No one strange to the court could
have gold rings nor pins nor jingling bangles of gold and
silver. Nobody without the royal consent had the right to
wear on his clothes gilding of any sort; but the authorization
once granted, one might wear it indefinitely. When a man presented himself at the palace, if he had a vesture falling beneath the girdle, if his *kris* was not attached in front, if he
was not clad in a *sabec,* he was not admitted, whatever might
be his distinction. If anyone entered with his *kris* attached
behind, the officer took it away from him.

Such were formerly the prohibitions of the Malay kings.
Whoever transgressed was guilty of *lèse-majesté* and was condemned to pay a fine of one to five katis. White parasols were
held in higher esteem than yellow ones, because they could be
seen at a greater distance. That is why they were ranked
higher; the first were for the King and the second for the
princes. The objects of the king's private use, such as the
spittoon, the ewer for his ablutions, the fan, and other like
objects, had no fixed place, except the betel-tray and the sword,
which they kept at the right and left of the sovereign. At the
arrival and departure of an ambassador, the servitors of the
King brought from the palace dishes and basins which were
received by the head of the *bataras* and deposited near the
bendahari. They gave a dish and a scarf to the bearer of the

letter. If the missive came from Pasey or from Harau, it was received with all the royal pomp—drum, flute, trumpet, kettle-drum, and two white parasols together; but the bugle did not figure at this reception. The ministers preceded the elephant bearing the message, the *bataras* followed it with the *sida-sida*. The letter was borne by the chief of the *bedaouenda*, and they placed the elephant at the extremity of the *balei*. For the kings of these two countries were equal in greatness to the King of Malaka. Younger or older, all gave the salaam.

Having reached the audience-chamber, the letter was received by the chief of heralds of the right, the one of the left being charged with transmitting the words of the King to the ambassador, and the herald of the right transmitted the answer. If the message came from another country than Pasey and Harau, they suppressed part of the men. The *cortège* included only the drum, the flute, and a yellow parasol. They took, as was suitable, now an elephant, now a horse, and they halted outside the first exterior gate. When the message came from a more considerable sovereign, they employed the flute and two parasols, one white and one yellow. The elephant passed through the exterior gate, for formerly the royal entrance included seven fortifications. At his departure, the ambassador received a complete investiture, even were he only a simple ambassador of Rakan. The same gift was offered to our own ambassadors at the moment of their departure.

When the King conferred a title, he gave audience in the *falerong*, with the following procedure: According to the rank, the person to be honored was brought on an elephant, on horseback, or simply on foot, with parasol, drum, and flute. There were green, blue, and red parasols. The noblest were the yellow and the white, which with the kettle-drums represented the height of distinction. The yellow with the trumpet was also very distinguished; they were the parasols of the princes and greatest personages. The violet, red, and green parasols were those of the *sida-sida*, of the *bataras*, and of the *houlou balongs*. The blue and black ones served for any other person summoned to receive a title. When the personage arrived at the palace, he was detained without. Then they read before the King a very fine piece. It was a descendant of Batl that held this office. The piece read, they took it out.

He who received it was of the family of the candidate for
honors. With this piece they brought a *tetampan* scarf with
which the reader invested the candidate, whom he then introduced into the audience-chamber. There a mat was stretched
for him to sit upon in whatever place the King designated.

Then arrived the vestments. For a personage promoted
to the ranks of the *bendahari* there were five trays. The sons
of radjas and the grand officers had four trays only, and so on
down through the various ranks. The servitors of the King
charged with this duty approached the beneficiary and placed
the vestments upon his shoulders. He crossed his arms, to
hold the vestments in place, and they took him outside. The
etiquette in that was the same for ambassadors awarded an
investiture, each according to the rights of his rank. The
beneficiary dressed himself outside and then re-entered. They
decorated him with a frontlet and with bracelets, for every
man who received a title wore bracelets, each according to his
dignity. Some had bracelets in the form of a dragon with
amulets, others had bracelets of precious stones, others of blue
enamel, others of silver. These wore them on both wrists, those
on only one. The beneficiary thus decorated went and bowed
before the King. Then he returned accompanied according to
his rank, or by the person who introduced him. The *cortège*
included now a drum and a flute alone, now trumpets or kettle-
drums, sometimes a white parasol; but the white parasol was
a rare honor, as well as the kettle-drums, for the yellow parasol and the trumpet were very hard to obtain in those times.

On festival days, when the King went forth in a palanquin,
he was surrounded by high officers of state. At the head,
before the sovereign, marched the *bataras* and the *houlou
balongs*, each following their charge. Footmen, also before
the King, bore the royal insignia. The royal pikes were at the
right and left; the *bataras* had sword at shoulder. Before
them marched the lancers. When the King gives a festival it
is the *panghoulou bendahari* who arranges everything inside the
palace, stretches mats, decorates the *balerong*, and places the
bangings on the ceilings. It is he who looks after the repasts
and sends the invitations; for the servitors of the King, his
bendahari, his tax-gatherers, and the receiver of the port all
depend on the administration of the *panghoulou bendahari*.

He invites the guests and the *temonggoreg* seats them. In the hall the guests eat four at a dish, to the end of the platform. If any one of the various fours are lacking the others eat without him, by threes or by twos or even one alone. For it is not permitted for those below to ascend to make up the number. The *bendahari* eats alone or from the same dish as the princes.

Such was in former days the etiquette of Malaka. There were many other regulations, but to relate them all would weary the attentions of my readers. At the month of Ramadhau, at the twenty-seventh night, while it was still light, they went in state to make adorations to the mosque. The *Temonggoreg* was at the head of the elephant. They first took in state to the mosque the betel-tray, the royal insignia, and the drum. When night came, the King started for the mosque, following the ceremonial of festival days, made the prayer of perfumes, and returned.

The next day the *laksamana* carried in state the turban, for the Malay kings were accustomed to go to the mosque in a turban, a *badjon,* and a *sarong.* These vestments were forbidden at weddings except by express permission. It was also forbidden to dress in the Hindoo fashion. Only those persons who had worn this costume for a long time were allowed to wear it at prayers and at weddings. Festival days, great or small, the *bendahari* and the grandees assembled at the palace, and the *panghoulou bendahari* brought in pomp the palanquin. As soon as they saw it appear, the persons seated in the *balei* descended and stood about. Seven times they beat upon the drum, and each time the trumpet sounded. After the sev 'h, the King set out on an elephant and came to the platform erected for that purpose, which he mounted. At sight of him, all those present bowed to the earth, except the *bendahari,* who mounted the platform to receive him. The palanquin having approached, the King placed himself in it, and they started for the mosque according to the ceremonial above mentioned.

Such was formerly the etiquette of the Malay kings. Such I learned it, such I tell it. If I commit any error, I desire to be convicted by anyone who has given attention to this story, and implore the indulgence of the reader.

THE PRINCESS DJOUHER-MANIKAM

—

[*Translated by Aristide Marre and Chauncey C. Starkweather*]

THE PRINCESS DJOUHER-MANIKAM

THIS is the history of the Princess Djouher-Manikam,
whose renown is celebrated in all lands, windward and
leeward.

There was in the city of Bagdad a king named Haroun-er-
Raschid, sovereign of a vast empire. He was a prince who
feared God the almighty, and worthy of all praise, for he was
a king descended from the prophet. After having lived for
some time in his kingdom, he desired to start on a pilgrimage.
So he addressed his ministers and his military chiefs and spoke
to them as follows:

" O you all, my subjects, my officers, what is your opinion?
I would fain make a pilgrimage to the house of God."

The cadi, prostrating himself, answered: " Sire, King of
the world, the will of your sublime Majesty is very just, but in
my opinion your departure would cause the ruin of the inhabitants of the fields, and those of your subjects who accompany you will have much to suffer."

The prince, having heard these words, said: " The opinion
of the cadi is loyal, and you, my officers, tell what is your
advice."

The officers arose, then they prostrated themselves and
spoke as follows: " Sire, King of the world, we, your
servants, beg you a thousand and a thousand times to cause
your forgiveness to descend upon our heads, but how will
your Majesty accomplish the pilgrimage? In whom can you
trust to protect the country and watch over the palace?"

The prince having heard these words of his officers, none
of whom approved of the pilgrimage, kept silence and restrained his anger, and then departed and returned to the
palace. Some days after this, by the will of the most high
God, the heart of the prince felt more keenly still the desire
to make the pilgrimage. He gave orders to gather together

the interpreters of the law, the wise men, and the *muftis*, as
well as the officers.   When they were all assembled, the prince
went to the audience-chamber, and there before the officers
of the court he questioned one of the doctors.   It was the
mufti of the city of Bagdad.   He, prostrating himself, said:
" The pilgrimage of his Majesty would be an excellent work,
but is it of absolute necessity?   For the voyage will be very
long, and there is no one, my lord, who would be capable of
ruling in the place of your sublime Majesty."

The prince answered: " He in whom we first of all place
our trust is God.   We shall hope then in the blessing of his
envoy.   We shall leave the cadi here, and if it pleases God
the most high, we shall return promptly as soon as we have
accomplished the pilgrimage."

The King therefore caused to be equipped and provided
with all sorts of provisions, those of his subjects who were
going to accompany him, and when the favorable moment
had arrived he started with the Queen, some of the maids-of-
honor, and his son named Minbah Chahaz.   He took his son,
but he left behind, guarded in the palace, his daughter called
the Princess Djouher-Manikam.   In those times there was
no one in the country of Bagdad who surpassed in beauty the
Princess Djouher-Manikam.   Furthermore, she had in her
heart the fear of God the most high and worthy of all praise,
and would not cease her prayers.

After travelling for some time, the prince her father arrived
at Mecca, and fulfilled his duties as a pilgrim.   He recited the
appropriate prayers.   But observing that there was still a
great quantity of provisions, the prince said to his officers:

" It is good for us to wait a year or so, for our provisions
are yet considerable."

The officers replied: " It is well, lord of the world!   Whatever may be your Majesty's commands, we place them above
our heads."   " Since it is thus," answered the prince, " it is
fitting that we should send a letter thus conceived: ' Peace
and blessing upon the cadi: I place my trust in God first of
all, and in the cadi, to guard my kingdom, palace, and my
child the Princess Djouher-Manikam.   Be a faithful guardian,
neglect nothing in the cares to be given to my kingdom, for
I am going to remain another year for the great pilgrimage.' "

The prince's letter reached the cadi. The latter gave all his efforts to the good administration of the country, and, according to the words of the prince, he avoided every negligence.

But one night while he was on watch near the fortifications of the King's palace, Satan came to him and slid into his heart a temptation. The cadi thought in his heart: "The King's daughter is of a marvellous beauty; her name, Djouher-Manikam, is charming; and her face is lovely. Since it is thus, I must marry this daughter of the King." The cadi called the man who was guarding the gate, exclaiming:

"Ho! Guardian of the gate! Open unto me."

The guardian of the gate demanded, "Who is there?"

The cadi replied, "It is I, the cadi."

So the guardian promptly opened the gate, and the cadi entered within the fortification, then went up into the palace and found the princess there saying her evening prayers. He hid behind the lamp in a corner which was dark. When her prayer was finished, the Princess Djouher-Manikam cast her eyes in that direction and saw there was someone standing there in the shadow, so three times again she said the "verse of the Throne"; but she saw that the vision had not yet vanished from her eyes.

Then the princess said in her heart: "What in the world is that? Is it a ghost? Is it a demon? Is it a djinn? If it were, it would have necessarily disappeared when I recited the 'verse of the Throne.'"

The cadi heard these words and said: "O Princess Djouher-Manikam, it is I, the cadi."

"What are you doing here?" asked the princess. He answered, "I wish to marry you."

The Princess Djouher-Manikam said: "O cadi! Why do you act so to me? Have you then no fear of God the most high and worthy of all praise? Do you not blush before the face of my ancestor the prophet Mahomet, the envoy of God? May the peace and blessings of God be upon him! As for me, I am the servant of the Lord and I belong to the religion of the envoy of God. I fear to marry now. And you, cadi, why do you act so? My father gave you a charge. He sent you a letter which commanded you to protect the country and all who dwelt in his palace. Why do you conduct yourself in this fashion toward me?"

The cadi, hearing these words of the Princess Djouher-Manikam, felt a great confusion in his heart. He went out of the palace and returned home full of trouble and emotion. When it was day, the cadi sent a letter to the King Haroun-er-Raschid at Mecca. It was thus conceived: "Your Majesty left me to be guardian of his kingdom, his palace, and his daughter. Now, the Princess Djouher-Manikam desires to marry me. This is the reason why I send this letter to your Majesty." Thus spake the cadi in his letter.

When it reached the prince and he had read it, he immediately summoned his son Minbah-Chahaz. He came in haste, and the King gave him a cutlass and said, "Return to Bagdad and slay your sister, because she will bring shame upon the family by marrying now."

Minbah-Chahaz bowed before his father. Then he set out to return to his own country.

Arriving at the end of his journey, he entered the city, and went up to the palace of the Princess Djouher-Manikam. She was filled with joy and said, "Welcome, O my brother!"

Minbah-Chahaz answered, "O my little sister, our parents will remain for the great pilgrimage."

The brother and sister thus chatting together, the Princess Djouher-Manikam said, "O my brother, I wish to sleep."

"It is well, my sister," answered Minbah-Chahaz; "sleep while your brother combs his little sister's hair." And the princess Djouher-Manikam slept.

Her brother then took a cushion, which he slipped under the head of the young virgin his sister; then he thought in his heart: "If I do not execute the commands of my father, I shall be a traitor to him. But, alas, if I kill my sister, I shall not have a sister any more. If I do not kill her, I shall certainly commit a crime against the most high, because I shall not have obeyed the order of my father. I will fulfil then my father's will. It is a duty obligatory on all children. What good are these subterfuges?" His resolution thus confirmed, he bound his handkerchief over his eyes and directed his cutlass against his sister's neck. But at that instant, by the will of God the most high, a little gazelle came up and, by the power of God the most high, placed its neck upon the neck of the princess Djouher-Manikam, saying, " I will take the place of the princess Djouher-Manikam." And the little gazelle was killed by Minbah-Chahaz. That done he unbound his eyes and saw a little gazelle lying dead with its throat cut, by the side of his young sister the princess Djouher-Manikam.

At this sight, Minbah-Chahaz was stricken with astonishment. He thought in his heart: " Since it is so with my sister, she must be entirely innocent, and cannot have commited the least fault. Nevertheless, although I am confident that she was calumniated by the cadi I must tell my father that I have killed her."

Minbah-Chahaz set out then for Mecca, to find the prince his father. When he had arrived at Mecca he presented to his father the cutlass still stained with blood. The King Harouner-Raschid cried, " Praise be to God, the Lord of the worlds. Our shame is now effaced, since you have poniarded your sister and she is dead." Such were the deeds of this first story.

The princess Djouher-Manikam, having awakened after the departure of Minbah-Chahaz, saw that her brother was no longer there, but that at her side there was a little gazelle with its throat cut. She thought in her heart: " The cadi has slandered me to my father, and that is why my brother came here with orders to kill me." The princess Djouher-Manikam felt a great shame and thought in her heart, " Since it is so, I must retire to a hidden place." Now in the King's park there was a solitary place in the midst of a vast deserted plain. There was a pond of very agreeable appearance there, many kinds of fruit-trees and flowers, and an oratory beautifully built. The princess Djouher-Manikam set out and retired to this place to pray to God the most high and worthy of all praise. She was established there for some time when, by the will of God the most high, a certain thing happened.

SECOND STORY

There was in the country of Damas a king who was named
Radja Chah Djouhou. This King wished to go hunting in the
deserted forests. His first minister said to him, bowing low:
" O my lord, King of the world, why does your Majesty wish
to go hunting in foreign countries? "

King Chah Djouhou replied: " I insist upon my plan of
going to hunt in foreign lands, in forests far removed from
ours. I wish to go from place to place, from plain to plain.
Such is my will." The prince set out therefore accompanied
by his ministers, his chiefs, and his servants.

They had all been hunting for some time and had not yet
found a single bit of game. The prince had directed his march
toward the forests of the country of Bagdad. These forests
were of immense extent. The heat was excessive, and the
prince, being very thirsty, wanted a drink of water. The
people who generally carried water for the King said to him:
" O lord, sovereign of the world, your Majesty's provision
of water is entirely exhausted."

The prince then asked of his officers and servants: " Which
of you can get me water? I will reward him with riches and
with slaves."

These words were heard by one of his officers named Asraf-
el-Kaum. He said: " O my lord, sovereign of the world,
give me the vase which will serve for water, and I will go and
seek water for your Majesty."

Then the prince said to the people who had brought water
for his use, " Give my emerald pitcher into the hands of Asraf-
el-Kaum."

The latter bowed low and started to seek water. Seeing
from afar a very large fig-tree, he advanced in that direction.
Arriving near the tree he saw at its base an oratory and a
pond. At the oratory there was a woman of very great beauty.
The splendor of her countenance shone like that of the full
moon at its fourteenth day. Asraf-el-Kaum, astonished and
moved with admiration, thought in his heart: " Is this a
human creature, or is it a peri? " and Asraf-el-Kaum saluted
the princess Djouher-Manikam, who returned the salutation.

Then the princess asked him, "What is your desire in coming here to my dwelling?"

Asraf-el-Kaum answered, "I have come here to ask you for water, for I have lost my way."

The princess said, "Take water, lord."

Asraf-el-Kaum plunged the emerald pitcher into the pond, and filled it with water. Then he asked permission to return.

Arriving near the King Chah Djouhou he presented the pitcher to the prince, who seized it quickly and drank.

"Asraf-el-Kaum," said the prince, "where did you find such fresh and delicious water? In all my life I have never drunk the like."

Asraf-el-Kaum answered: "O my lord, sovereign of the world, there is a garden in the middle of the plain, and in this garden there is a very large and bushy fig-tree, and at the foot of this tree there is a pond, and near this pond there is an oratory. At this oratory there was a woman who was reading the Koran. This charmingly beautiful woman has no equal in this world. I saluted her and then returned to the presence of the sovereign of the world. That is what I saw, my lord."

"Conduct me to this place," said the King.

"O sovereign of the world, if your Majesty wishes to go thither, let it be with me alone. Let not my lord take his people with him, for it is a woman, and naturally she would be ashamed."

The prince set out then on horseback with Asraf-el-Kaum. The princess Djouher-Manikam, seeing two cavaliers approach, thought in her heart: "I must hide myself, so that I may not be seen." So she left the oratory and went toward the fig-tree. She addressed a prayer to God the most high and worthy of all praise, in these terms:

"O God, I beseech thee, give me a refuge in this tree, for thy servant, O Lord, is ashamed to look upon the faces of these infidels."

Then by the will of God the most high, the tree opened in two and the princess Djouher-Manikam entered by the split, and the tree closed and became as it was before. The King Chah Djouhou and Asraf-el-Kaum arrived at the oratory, but the prince saw nothing of the princess Djouher-Manikam. He was astonished and said:

"O Asraf-el-Kaum, the woman has gone. But just a moment ago I saw her from afar, seated at the oratory, and now she has suddenly disappeared." The prince added: "O Asraf-el-Kaum, perhaps, as with the prophet Zachariah (upon whom be blessings!), her prayer has been answered and she has entered this tree."

Then he offered this prayer to God the most high and worthy, of all praise: "O God, if thou wilt permit that this woman be united to thy servant, then grant her to him."

The prayer of the King Chah Djouhou was heard, and a woman of dazzling beauty appeared before his eyes. He desired to seize her, but the princess Djouher-Manikam pronounced these words: "Beware of touching me, for I am a true believer." Hearing these words the King Chah Djouhou drew back, a little ashamed. Then he said:

"Woman, what is your country? Whose child are you, and what is your name?"

The princess answered: "For a long time I have dwelt here, and I have no father nor mother. My name is Djouher-Manikam."

The King, hearing these words of the princess Djouher-Manikam, took off his cloak and gave it to the princess, who covered all her body with it. Then she got up and descended to the ground. Then King Chah Djouhou, dismounting from his horse, received her, put her on his horse, and took her to the country of Damas.

Asraf-el-Kaum then said to the King: "O my lord, sovereign of the world, you made a promise to your servant. Be not careless nor forgetful, my lord."

"Asraf-el-Kaum, be not disturbed. I will fulfil my promise to you. If it pleases God, when I have arrived in our own country, I shall certainly give you all that I promised you." King Chah Djouhou set out for the country of Damas.

After a certain time on the way, the prince came to the city of Damas and entered his palace. He commanded one of his pages to summon the cadi, and a page went promptly to call him. The latter, in all haste, entered the presence of the King. Chah Djouhou said: "O cadi, marry me to the princess

Djouher-Manikam." And the cadi married them. After the celebration of the marriage the prince Chah Djouhou gave to Asraf-el-Kaum 1,000 dinars and some of his slaves, both men and women. King Djouhou and Princess Djouher-Manikam were happy and full of tenderness for each other. Within a few years the princess had two sons, both very beautiful. The prince loved these children very fondly. But above all he loved his wife. He was full of tender solicitude for her, and bore himself with regard to her with the same careful atention that a man uses who carries oil in the hollow of his hand. Some time later Princess Djouher-Manikam had another son of great beauty. The prince loved this third child tenderly. He gave him a great number of nurses and governesses, as is the custom for the children of the greatest kings. And he never ceased to bestow upon him the most watchful care.

It happened one day that the ministers, the chiefs, and the courtiers of the King, all gathered in his presence, were enjoying all sorts of sport and amusements. The prince showed himself very joyous, and the princess herself played and amused herself with the three children. Her countenance shone with the brightness of rubies; but happening to think of her father, her mother, and her brother, she began to weep and said: "Alas, how unhappy I am! If my father, mother, and brother could see my three children, necessarily their affection for me would be greater." And the princess Djouher-Manikam burst into sobs. The prince, who was not far from there, heard her, and as the princess did not stop weeping he asked her: "O princess, why do you weep thus? What do I lack in your eyes? Is it riches or physical beauty or noble birth? Or is it the spirit of justice? Tell me what is the cause of your tears?"

Princess Djouher-Manikam answered: Sovereign of the world, your Majesty has not a single fault. Your riches equal those of Haroun. Your beauty equals that of the prophet Joseph (peace be upon him!). Your extraction equals that of the envoy of God (Mahomet). May the benediction of God and blessings rest upon him! Your justice equals that of King Rouchirouan. I don't see a single fault in you, my lord."

King Chah Djouhou said: "If it is thus, why then does my princess shed tears?"

Princess Djouher-Manikam answered: "If I wept thus while playing with my three children, it is because I thought that if my father, my mother, and my brother should see my three children, necessarily their affection for me would be greater. And that is why I shed tears."

King Chah Djouhou said to her: "O my young wife, dear princess, are your father and mother still living? What is your father's name?"

Princess Djouher-Manikam answered, "O my lord, my father is named Haroun-er-Raschid, King of Bagdad."

Clasping her in his arms and kissing her, the prince asked her: "Why, until this day have you not told the truth to your husband?"

And the princess answered: "I wished to avow the truth, but perhaps my lord would not have had faith. It is on account of the children that I tell the truth."

King Chah Djouhou answered: "Since it is so, it is fitting that we should start, and make a visit upon King Haroun-er-Raschid."

He called his ministers, ordered them to make all the preparations, and commanded them to place in order ingots of gold and ingots of silver on which were graven the name of King Haroun-er-Raschid; and his ministers' vestments woven of goats' hair and fine wool, stuffs of price, many kinds of superb precious stones of various colors, formed the burden of forty camels, which bore these presents to the King, his father-in-law, in the city of Bagdad.

During the night Princess Djouher thought in her heart: "If the two kings meet, there will necessarily be discord, and at the end separation." Having thus thought she said to her husband: "O sovereign of the world, do not set out at the same time with me, for in my opinion the meeting of the two kings would have as a final result a disagreement. Permit me therefore to start first with the three children, that I may present them to my father and mother. Give the command to conduct me to the country of Bagdad, near my father, to whomsoever you shall judge worthy of your confidence for this mission."

When the prince heard these words of the princess whom he loved so tenderly and whose wishes he granted, he ordered his ministers and chiefs to arrange the transport of the princess and her children. Addressing the ministers he said as follows: "O you my ministers, whom among you can I charge to conduct safely my wife and three children to Bagdad, near their ancestor King Haroun-er-Raschid?"

No one among them dared approach and speak. All held silence. Then the prince, addressing the oldest minister of all, said:

"O my minister, it is you to whom, following the dictates of my heart, I can trust to accompany my wife and three children. For I have always found you loyal and faithful to me. Beside, you are older than the other ministers. And you have the fear of God the most high and worthy of all praise as well as respect for your King."

The minister said: "O my lord, it is in all sincerity that your servant puts above his head the commands of your Majesty. I shall do my whole duty in conducting the princess and her children to the King Haroun-er-Raschid."

So the King Chah Djouhou trusted his wife and his three children to this perfidious minister, reposing upon the promise he had made. Forty camels were laden with presents, forty nurses for the children, one hundred ladies in the suite of the princess, a thousand cavaliers, well armed and well equipped, formed the escort. The princess took leave of her husband. He held her clasped in his arms, and, weeping, covered her and his three children with kisses. He bade her to present his homage to her father the Sultan Haroun-er-Raschid, his salutations to her elder brother Minbah-Chahaz, and to place at the feet of their majesties a thousand and a thousand apologies, and to make his excuses to her brother Minbah-Chahaz. Then the prince said to the wicked minister:

"O my minister, you must go now, and lead the camel of my wife, for I have perfect confidence in you. Above all, guard her well."

But the King did not lean upon God the most high and worthy of all praise, and that is why God punished him.

When the prince had finished speaking to the minister the latter said: "O my lord, King of the world, your servant bears your command on his head." So the cavalcade started on the march. Princess Djouher-Manikam mounted her camel with her three children. A body-guard held the van. She proceeded accompanied by the wretched minister and all the escort, wending from day to day toward the city of Bagdad. They had reached one of the halting-places when day was turning into night. The minister then erected a tent so that the princess might repose in it. The people put up their tents all about. Princess Djouher-Manikam dismounted from her camel and entered the tent, with her three children. The tents of the nurses and ladies-in-waiting surrounded the tent of the princess in a circle. In the middle of the night a violent rain began to fall. Then the wretched minister, stirred by Satan, was stirred in his heart. He thought: " The King's wife is most beautiful; beautiful, indeed, as her name, Djouher-Manikam. I must marry her."

So the rebel minister started, and entered the tent of the princess, and asked her to marry him. He found her seated by her three children, occupied in chasing away the mosquitoes. When the princess saw him enter her tent she asked him: " O my minister, what brings you to my tent at this hour in the middle of the night?"

The minister answered, " I have come to beg you to marry me."

The princess then said: " Is that what brings you here? And it was to you that the King intrusted me on account of your great age, and as if you were my father. It was in you that he put all his confidence that you would take us safely, me and my children, to my venerable father, King Haroun-er-Raschid. What must be your nature, that you should so betray his trust?"

The wretched minister replied: " If you refuse to marry me, I will kill your children."

" Never," said the princess, " never shall I consent to marry you. And if you kill my children, what can I do against the decree of God, save to invoke his name?"

The minister killed one of the children. When it was dead, he made the same demand on the princess for the second time, and she answered: " Never shall I consent to marry you."

The minister said: " If you refuse, I shall kill another of your children."

The Princess Djouher-Manikam answered: "If you slay my child, it is by the decree of God, and I submit to his will." The minister killed the second child.

"No," repeated the princess. "Never shall I consent to wed you."

The wretched minister said: "Then I will kill your third child."

"If you kill him, what can I do but to submit to the will of God, and invoke his name?" The third son of the King was killed.

Questioned anew, the princess said again, "Never shall I marry you."

And the wicked minister said: "If you will not marry me, I will kill you, too."

Then the princess thought in her heart: "If I do not appear to yield, he will kill me, too, without a doubt. I must employ a trick." Then she said: "Await me here, until I wash from my clothes and my body the stains of my children's blood."

The minister accursed of God replied: "Very well. I await you here."

Then the princess Djouher went out of her tent. The rain was falling in torrents. The princess, fleeing precipitately, walked during the whole night, not knowing where she was going. She had walked many hours when day broke. The princess arrived thus near a tree in the midst of the plain, and, having measured its height with her eyes, she climbed into it. At this moment there passed along the road a merchant who had made his sales and was returning to the city of Bassrah. His name was Biyapri. Passing beneath the tree he raised his eyes and beheld a woman seated in the tree.

"Who are you?" he said; "are you woman or djinn?"

"I am neither demon nor djinn, but a descendant of the prophet of God (may blessings rest upon him), a disciple of the prophet Mahomet, envoy of God."

Biyapri climbed up the tree, put her on his camel, and taking up his journey conducted her to the country of Bassrah. Arriving at his house he desired to marry her. But she put him off saying: "Wait, for I have made a solemn vow before God not to look upon the face of a man for forty days. When the time expires, that will be possible. But if these forty days have not yet run I should surely die." So Biyapri installed her on his latticed roof and lavished attention and care upon her.

Immediately after the flight of the princess Djouher-Mani-kam the minister commanded the whole escort to return and present itself to the King Chah Djouhou. He said to his people: "O all your servants of the Queen, see what has been her conduct. Her three children are dead, and it is she who killed them. After that she disappeared. Where has she taken refuge? Nobody in the world knows that. As for you, depart, bear the bodies of his three children to King Chah Djouhou, and tell him all the circumstances."

Arriving in the presence of the King, they reported all the circumstances of the minister's treachery toward the princess, and the murder of his three children. They added that the minister had departed, leaving word that he had gone to find the princess, and had taken with him his own three sons, forty soldiers, and the treasure.

When the prince had heard these words he was struck with a stupor. But his sorrow at having let the princess go without him was useless. He caused the three young princes to be buried. The King shed tears, and all the people of the household filled the air with cries and sobs, so that the noise seemed like the bursts of thunder, while the funeral ceremonies were proceeding according to the customs of the greatest kings. After that the King descended from his royal throne and became a dervish, the better to seek in all lands his well-beloved spouse. He had with him three slaves only. One of them was named Hestri.

"Go," he said to him, "go seek your mistress in all countries." And he gave him a horse and some provisions.

Hestri said: "May your Majesty be happy! O lord, King of the world, whatever be your commands, your servant places them upon his head." Hestri bowed low, then mounted his horse and rode away toward the city of Bassrah.

After proceeding some time he reached Bassrah, and passed by the house of Biyapri. At this very moment the princess Djouher-Manikam was sitting on the roof of Biyapri's house. She looked attentively at the face of Hestri as he was passing by the house and called to him saying: "Hestri, what brings you here?"

Hestri, casting his glance toward the roof, saw the princess Djouher-Manikam and said to her: "I was sent by your husband to seek you, princess."

She replied: "Go away, for the present. Come back when it is night. As it is broad daylight now I fear lest Biyapri should discover our departure."

Hestri, bowing low, replied, "Very well, princess." He walked here and there, waiting till night should come. When it was dark he returned to the house of Biyapri and waited a few minutes. Then he called the princess.

"Wait," she said, "for Biyapri is still watching." Hestri stooped down, and fell asleep near Biyapri's house, having first of all tied the bridle of the horse to his girdle.

The princess Djouher-Manikam descended from the roof, and mounted the horse while Hestri was yet sleeping. She sat on the horse waiting till Hestri should awake. But an Æthiopian robber, who had come to rob the storehouse of Biyapri, saw the horse whose bridle was attached to the belt of Hestri. He unfastened the bridle and led the horse to the middle of the plain. In the mind of the princess it was Hestri who was thus leading the horse. But the moon having risen, the Æthiopian saw seated upon the horse a woman of a striking and marvellous beauty. The heart of the Æthiopian was filled with joy. He said in his heart:

"For a very long time have I been stealing riches. Truly, I have acquired no small store of jewels, pearls, precious stones, gold and silver, and magnificent vestments of all sorts. But all that is nothing in comparison with the marvel I have just now found and who will become my wife, the light of my eyes, and the fruit of my heart. Now shall I enjoy in peace the happiness of having such a wife."

The house of the Æthiopian robber was seated on the top of a hill. He conducted the princess thither, showed her all it contained, and gave it to her, saying: "O my future bride, it is to you that all which this house contains belongs. Make use of it according to your good pleasure." The princess said, "First of all, be tranquil." And she thought in her heart: "This is my destiny. First I was with Biyapri, and now I have fallen into the hands of an Æthiopian robber. It is by the will of God that this has happened to his servant." The Æthiopian robber was bent on having the marriage celebrated at once, but the princess said: " I cannot be married now, for I have made a vow to God the most high not to see the face of a man for three days."

The Æthiopian robber desired to drink, and said: " Come, let us drink together."

" In my opinion," observed the princess, " if we begin to drink both together you will become heavy with wine, and I, too. Then they will take me far from you and kill you. Come, I will fill your cup and you shall drink first. When you have drunk enough, then I will drink in my turn, and you shall fill my cup."

The Æthiopian robber was very joyful at these words of the princess. " What you say is true," said he. He received with great pleasure the cup from the hands of the princess and drank. After emptying the cup many times he fell down in the stupor of intoxication, losing his senses and becoming like a dead man. The princess Djouher-Manikam put on a magnificent costume of a man, and adding a weapon something like a *kandjar*, went out of the house. Then mounting her horse she rode forward quickly and came to the foot of the hill. She directed her course toward the country of Roum, and continuing her journey from forest to forest, and from plain to plain, she reached the gate of the fortifications of the city of Roum at the moment when the King of that country had just died.

When the princess Djouher-Manikam had arrived outside the fortifications of Roum, she sat down in the *baley*, near the fort. She was marvellously beautiful, and her vestments, all sparkling with gold, were adorned with precious stones, pearls, and rubies. A man happening to pass by saw her, and was seized with astonishment and admiration. For in the country of Roum there was nobody who could compare with this young man, so handsome and so magnificently attired. He asked:

" Whence come you and why did you come here? "

The princess answered: " I know not the place where I am at this moment. I came from the city of Damas."

This citizen of Roum took leave and went away to present himself to the vezir and tell what he had seen. The vezir, having heard him, went out promptly to find the young man. As soon as he had approached him and had seen his remarkable beauty and his splendid vestments decorated with precious stones, pearls, and rubies, the vezir seated himself by him and said:

" Young man, whence do you come, and why did you come to this land? "

The princess answered: " I wish to travel through the world for my pleasure. That is my will."

The vezir replied: " Would you like to have us make you King of this country? " The princess replied: " For what reason should I wish to be king in this country? And by what means could it be achieved? "

The vezir replied: " Our King is dead."

" Is there no child? " asked the princess.

" The King has left a child," answered the vezir, " but he is still very little, and incapable of governing his subjects. That is why we will make you King of this country."

The princess Djouher-Manikam answered: " Why not? What prevents? If you all will follow my counsel I will accept the throne of this country."

The ministers said, " And why should we not follow the commands of my lord? "

The vezir conducted her to the palace. All the ministers of state and the high officers assembled to proclaim as their king the princess Djouher-Manikam. That done, the princess took the name of Radja Chah Djouhou.

After reigning some time her spirit of justice and her perfect equity in the government of her subjects rendered her name celebrated in all the foreign countries. Radja Chah Djouhou said to her minister:

" O minister, have built for me a *baley* outside the fort." And the ministers and the officers commanded them in haste to construct the *baley*. As soon as it was built they came to announce it to the King. The latter said:

" O my vezir, is there in my kingdom a man who knows how to paint? "

" Yes, my lord, king of the world, there is a very skilful painter here."

"Let him come to me."

"Immediately, my lord," said the vezir, and he ordered a slave to go and summon the painter. The painter came in all haste and entered the presence of Radja Chah Djouhou, bowing his head to the floor. The prince said to him:

"O painter, have you a daughter who knows how to paint?"

The painter answered: "Yes, my lord, king of the world, I have a daughter very skilful in the art of painting."

"Tell your child to come here."

The painter bowed again and went to find his daughter. "O my child," he said, "the fruit of my heart, come, the King calls you."

Then the painter's daughter quickly set out, accompanied by her father. They together entered the presence of the King, who was still surrounded by his ministers and his officers. The painter and his daughter bowed their heads to the floor. The prince said:

"Painter, is this your daughter?"

"O my lord, king of the world, yes, this is my daughter."

"Come with me into the interior of the palace." And at the same time the prince started and entered his apartments, followed by the daughter of the painter. He led the way to a retired place, and said: "My daughter, make my portrait, I pray you, and try to have the resemblance good." Then the princess Djouher-Manikam clothed herself in woman's raiment, and in this costume she was ravishingly beautiful. That done, she commanded the artist to paint her thus. She succeeded perfectly and the portrait was a remarkable likeness, for the daughter of the painter was very skilful. When her work was finished she received a large sum in gold. The prince said to her:

"Come, sister, let this remain a secret. Reveal it not to anyone in the world. If you tell it I will slay you, with your father and your mother."

The daughter of the painter said: "O my lord, king of the world, how could your servant disobey your Majesty's commands?" She bowed low, and asked permission to go home.

Radja Chah Djouhou, in the presence of his ministers and his subjects, said to the vizier: "O vizier, place this portrait in the *baley* outside the fort, and have it guarded by forty men. If anyone coming to this portrait begins to weep or kiss it, seize him and bring him before me." The portrait hung in the *baley,* and the vezir ordered an officer to guard it with forty soldiers.

When the Æthiopian robber came out of his drunken slumber he saw that the princess Djouher-Manikam was no longer in his house. So he went out-of-doors weeping, and took up his journey, going from country to country until he arrived at the city of Roum. There he saw a *baley,* and hanging there a portrait which bore a perfect resemblance to the princess Djouher-Manikam. Quickly he climbed to the *baley,* and, holding the portrait in his arms, he wept and covered it with kisses.

"O unhappy man that I am! Here is the portrait of my well-beloved for whom I was seeking. Where can she be?"

The guards of the *baley,* seeing the act of the Æthiopian, seized him and bore him before the King. They told the deed.

The prince said: "Æthiopian robber, why did you act thus in reference to this picture?"

The Æthiopian answered: "O my lord, king of the world, I ask you a thousand and a thousand pardons. Your servant will tell the truth. If they kill me I shall die; if they hang me I shall be lifted very high; if they sell me I shall be carried very far away. O king of the world, hear the words of your humble slave. A certain night I had started out to rob. I found a horse, and on its back there was a woman of the most marvellous beauty. I took her to my house. I fell asleep in my cups. My beloved one disappeared. I became mad, and so it is, O king of the world, that your slave came to the fort and saw the portrait hanging at the *baley.* This portrait is the faithful picture of my well-beloved. That is why I weep."

The prince said: "O my vezir, let this man be carefully guarded. Treat him well and give him plenty to eat." On the other hand, Biyapri, after forty days, mounting the roof, saw that the princess Djouher was no longer there. He became mad, abandoned his house and all his wealth, and, becoming a dervish, went from country to country seeking the princess Djouher-Manikam, without ever finding her. Coming to the country of Roum he saw the *baley* situated outside the fort, and stopped there. Then he saw the portrait, and, observing it with the closest attention, he began to weep. Then he took it in his arms and covered it with kisses.

" Alas, my well-beloved! " he cried, " here indeed is your picture, but where can I find you? " He was immediately seized by the guard and led before the King of Roum.

" Biyapri," said the prince, " whence do you come, and why did you act thus? " Biyapri answered: " O my lord, king of the world, your slave asks pardon a thousand and a thousand times. I will tell the whole truth. If they kill me, I shall die; if they hang me, I shall be lifted very high; if they sell me, I shall be taken very far away. When I was engaged in commerce I passed under a tree, and saw that in this tree there was a woman of the most marvellous beauty. I took her and carried her to the city of Bassrah and installed her on the roof of my storehouse. A certain night she disappeared without my knowing where she had gone. Then, O king of the world, I became as one mad and left my native land. Arriving at the country of Roum I saw a *baley* outside the fort and came to sit down there. Then, my lord, I saw the portrait hanging at the *baley*. It exactly resembles my beloved, whom I lost. I pressed it in my arms and covered it with kisses. Such is the truth, O king of the world."

The prince then said to his minister: " O minister, let this man be carefully guarded and give him food and clothes."

The King of Damas, after abdicating the throne, had left his kingdom, and in the costume of a dervish had started to travel through the different countries. Arriving at Roum, the King Chah Djouhou saw a *baley* situated outside of the fort, and went to sit down near it. The prince looking closely at the portrait, which was exactly like the princess Djouher-Manikam, burst into a flood of tears and exclaimed:

" Alas! Fruit of my heart, my well-beloved, light of my eyes! It is, indeed, your picture. But you, whom I seek, oh, where are you? "

Speaking thus, the prince took the portrait in his arms and covered it with kisses. Seeing this, the guards of the *baley* seized him and carried him before the King.

The King said to him: " My lord, whence do you come?

How have you wandered into this country? And why did you behave thus about my portrait?"

The King Chah Djouhou answered: "Know that my wife, who is named the princess Djouher-Manikam, has disappeared far from me. It is for that reason that I have left my kingdom, and that I, dressed as a dervish, have walked from country to country, from plain to plain, from village to village, seeking her whom I have never been able to find. But arriving in your Majesty's country I saw hanging at the *baley* that portrait, which is of a striking resemblance to my wife. It is for this reason that I wept in contemplating this picture."

The princess smiled, and at the same time her heart was softened at seeing the conduct of her husband. She said to her prime minister: "O my minister, I confide this person to your care. Treat him worthily, give him the best of food and a suite of attendants. He is the King of Damas."

The minister therefore, by command of the princess, departed and conducted the King of Damas to a fine house, furnished and equipped according to the needs of kings.

The minister took all the riches which had been intended as presents for the King Haroun-er-Raschid. The ingots of gold and of silver, the rich garments in fine stuffs of the country of Rouzoungga, as well as the vestments of the princess Djouher-Manikam and of her three children, were transported and sold in the city of Bagdad. But the King Haroun-er-Raschid, seeing that his name and that of his daughter, the princess Djouher-Manikam, were graven on these ingots of gold and silver, seized all these riches.

The minister of the country of Damas said, "These riches are mine."

On his side the King Haroun-er-Raschid said: "These riches are mine, for my name and that of my child are engraved on these ingots of gold and silver."

The minister said, "Since your Majesty declares that these treasures are yours, we must try this case in a court of justice."

The King of Bagdad answered: "It is well. We will go wherever you wish."

"Very well," said the minister; "let us go then before the

King of the country of Roum. That prince has the reputation of being extremely just. Each of us shall plead his cause."

The prince answered: "It is well." The minister replied: "O king of the world, let us start without delay."

So the King Haroun-er-Raschid set out with his son Min-bah-Chahaz, his chief warrior, and his soldiers. The cadi accompanied the prince. On his side, the minister of the country of Damas started, accompanied by his three sons and forty soldiers of the country of Damas. After proceeding some time, they arrived at the city of Roum and entered the fortifications. Each one of them presented himself before the King and pleaded his cause.

The King Haroun-er-Raschid expressed himself as follows: "O king of the world! I present myself before your Majesty to ask your impartial judgment. The minister of the country of Damas brought to Bagdad, among other precious objects, ingots of gold and ingots of silver, on which are engraved my name and that of my daughter, the princess Djouher-Manikam. I seized these, and come to your Majesty to decide my claim to them."

The King of Roum said: "If it pleases God the most high, this affair shall be judged with the best of my powers." The King of Roum continued: "My officers and you, my ministers and chiefs, seek all the divine inspiration to decide the difference existing between the King of Bagdad and the minister of Damas."

The officers bowed low and said: "O my lord, king of the world, whatever they may be, we shall put the commands of your Majesty above our heads and shall carry them out to the letter." And they deliberated on the character of the dispute.

The King of Bagdad declared: "These objects are precious to me, for they bear engraven upon them the names of myself and my child."

On the other hand, and at the same time, the minister Damas declared, "These precious objects are mine."

The ministers and chiefs were very much embarrassed, and said to the King: "O king of the world, we, all of us, are unable to judge this dispute. It is too difficult for us. Only the impartial judgment of your Majesty can decide it."

The prince said: "It is well. I will pronounce sentence, if it please God the most high, provided that you consent to accept it."

The King of Bagdad answered: "O king of the world, judge between us according to your impartial justice."

The King of Roum then said: "O minister of Damas, and you, King of Bagdad, is it the wish of both of you that I should give judgment according to the judgment of God the most high?"

And they both answered: "That is what we ask, the judgment of God."

The prince replied: "If you consent on both sides, it is well."

"I consent to it," said the minister of Damas.

"And I, too," said the King of Bagdad.

The King of Roum then spoke in these terms: "In conformity with the law of the most high God, I ask this question of the King of Bagdad: Have you a daughter?"

The King of Bagdad replied: "Yes, king of the world, I have a daughter and a son."

"And have you at present these two children?"

The King of Bagdad answered: "I have my son, but my daughter—I lost her."

The King of Roum, continuing, said: "What is the cause of the loss of your daughter?" The King of Bagdad answered: "O king of the world, hear my story. While I was gone on a pilgrimage with my wife and my son, whose name is Minbah-Chahaz, I left my daughter to watch over my palace. Arriving at the end of my pilgrimage, I sent home a letter to the cadi, conceived as follows: 'May peace be with the cadi: I shall wait still for the grand pilgrimage about a year longer. As for all that concerns my kingdom, my palace, and my daughter, the princess Djouher-Manikam, watch with greatest care, and beware of any negligence in the protection of my kingdom and my child.' Some time later the cadi sent me a letter at Mecca, couched in these words: 'O king of the world, your servant has received the command to watch over the palace and the princess. But the princess now desires to marry me.' After I had read the letter from the cadi I called my son Minbah-Chahaz, and said to him: 'Start at once for

Bagdad, and slay your sister.' My son Minbah-Chahaz started immediately for Bagdad, and killed his sister. Then he returned and found me at Mecca. His cutlass was still blood-stained. Then I cried: ' Praise be to God the Lord of the universe, our shame is effaced.' Such is my story, O king of the world."

The King of Roum said: "It is well. Now I shall pronounce judgment." And addressing the minister of Damas he said to him: "O minister of Damas, tell me the truth if you wish that at the day of judgment the prophet should intercede for you (may the peace and blessings of God be upon him!). Speak and tell the truth. Say whence come these riches, in order that I may pronounce my judgment between you."

The minister of the King of Damas said: " O my lord, king of the world, I will lay at the foot of your Majesty's throne the completed story from the beginning. I received a mission from the King Chah Djouhou: ' O my minister,' he said, ' start, I send you to the city of Bagdad, taking my three children to their grandfather, and my wife, the princess Djouher-Manikam, to her mother and her father, the King Haroun-er-Raschid.' I set out, therefore, with the escort which accompanied the princess Djouher-Manikam, and we arrived at our first halting-place. When it was night I erected a tent, and the people of the escort all put up tents around that of the princess. But Satan breathed into my heart a temptation. This thought came to me: ' The wife of the King is wonderfully beautiful, and she has such a pretty name! I will go and ask her to marry me.' So I entered her tent. At that moment she was seated by her sleeping children, occupied in keeping away the mosquitoes. The princess demanded, ' O my minister, why do you come here?' And I answered, ' I have come to ask you to marry me.' The princess said: ' Have you no fear of God the most high? No, I cannot marry you. What would become of me if I should do such a thing?' Then I said, ' If you will not agree to marry me, I will kill one of your children.' The princess answered: ' If you kill my child it will be by the judgment of God, and what can I do but to invoke his name?' Then I killed one of the children. When he was dead I asked again if she would marry me, and I killed another of the children. When this one was dead I asked the same question. The princess answered, ' I cannot marry when I am already married.' I said to her, ' If you will not, then I will kill the third of your children.' The princess Djouher-Manikam answered, ' If you kill my third child, it will be by the judgment of God, and what can I do but invoke his name, for I am only a woman?' So I killed the third child. After the death of this last child of the King, I put again my question to the princess. She would not consent to marry me. I said to her, ' If you don't, I will kill you.' She answered: ' If you kill me, it is the decree of God. But wait awhile, for I wish to wash my garments and cleanse the traces of my children's blood from my body.' I said, ' It is well. We will have the wedding-feast to-morrow.' She left the tent. It was raining in torrents. I could not discover where she went. Such is my story, O king of the world."

The King said, " Minister of the country of Damas, have you any sons?"

He answered, " Yes, my lord, king of the world, I have three sons."

The prince said: " Let your three sons come here, in order that I may give judgment quickly, according to the law instituted by the prophet (may the peace and blessings of God be upon him!). Behold what his law prescribes: The minister killed the children of the princess Djouher-Manikam. It is not, therefore, the minister who should be punished with death, but his children should be slain. The execution of this judgment will be the just application of the law of retaliation between the minister and the princess." .

The minister summoned his three sons. As soon as they had come, he pointed them to the King of Roum.

The latter said to his minister, " O minister, where is the Æthiopian whom they brought here?" The Æthiopian robber was brought out, and prostrated himself before the King of Roum.

The King of Roum said to him: " Æthiopian, return to your own country and change your mode of life. You will never see again the woman for whom you are seeking." And the prince gave him a *keti* of gold.

Then the prince said: " O my minister, where is Biyapri?

Let them bring him here." So they brought Biyapri. When he arrived he bowed low before the prince.

The prince said: "Biyapri, go back to your own country and change your conduct. The woman whom you seek you will never see again." And the prince made him a gift of two *keti* of gold.

The King of Roum then said: "Let all assemble. I am about to pronounce judgment between the King of Bagdad and the minister of Damas." The minister and the officers assembled therefore in the presence of the King, together with many of his subjects.

The King of Roum said: "O my executioner, let the three children of the minister of Damas be all killed; such is the divine command." So the children of the minister of Damas were all three killed.

After they were dead the prince said: "Minister, return to the country of Damas, with a rag for your girdle, and during your last days change your conduct. If you do not know it, I am the princess Djouher-Manikam, daughter of the Sultan of Bagdad, wife of Chah Djouhou, my lord, and the sister of Minbah-Chahaz. God has stricken your eyes with blindness on account of your crimes toward me. It is the same with the cadi of the city of Bagdad."

The minister of Damas, seized with fear, trembled in all his limbs. He cast himself at the feet of the princess Manikam, and thus prostrated he implored pardon a thousand and a thousand times. Then he returned to Damas all in tears, and overwhelmed with grief at the death of his three sons. The cadi, covered with shame on account of his treachery to the Sultan of Bagdad, fled and expatriated himself.

The King of Roum commanded them to bring the King Chah Djouhou and give him a garment all sparkling with gold, and he sent him to dwell in the company of his father-in-law, the Sultan of Bagdad, and his brother-in-law, the prince Minbah-Chahaz.

Then the princess Djouher-Manikam retired. She entered the palace and returned clad in the garments of a woman. She then went out, accompanied by ladies of the court, and went to present herself to her father, the Sultan of Bagdad. She bowed before her father, her brother the prince Minbah-Chahaz, and her husband, the King Chah Djouhou. The princess said: "O all of you, lords and warriors of the country of Roum, know that I am a woman, and not a man. Behold my father, the Sultan Haroun-er-Raschid, King of Bagdad. Behold my brother, whose name is Minbah-Chahaz; and behold my husband, the King Chah Djouhou, who reigns over the country of Damas. From the time when you placed me upon the throne of Roum, if I have committed any fault by error or by ignorance, you must excuse me, for constantly the servants of God commit faults by error or ignorance. It is only God alone who forgets not, nor neglects, and is free from error or ignorance."

The grandees of the country of Roum said: "Never has your Majesty committed the least fault, either by ignorance or by error, during the time you have reigned over the country of Roum. Nevertheless, among the judgments just now rendered there was a fault committed by your glorious Majesty. The minister killed, the princess killed, both did it voluntarily. It was a fault of judgment for the princess Djouher-Manikam to have killed the children of the minister, just as the minister committed a fault in killing the children of the princess. There was a likeness there. Still, if it pleases her Majesty to remain upon the throne of Roum, we should all be very glad of it."

The princess Djouher said: "I shall take leave of you, my lords. It is good that we should make the young prince king, and that he should replace me on the throne."

The ministers and the officers of Roum responded, "Whatever be the commands of your Majesty, we place them above our heads."

Then the princess made the royal prince her successor, and the ministers and officers and subjects all bowed low, placed their hands above their heads, and proclaimed him King.

The princess Djouher-Manikam said: "O my child, here are the last instructions your mother gives you: You must practise justice so that God will make strong your realm. To you, my ministers and officers, I confide my child. If he commits some faults by negligence or by ignorance, I pray you take them not too much to heart, for my child is young, and he has not yet attained all the maturity of his judgment."

The ministers and officers answered: "O your Majesty, may your prosperity grow forever! How could it be possible for us to disobey your commands?"

The princess replied: "O my child, above all must you observe justice and be patient and liberal toward your ministers and officers and all your subjects, so that the favors of God may increase upon your person and that your kingdom may be protected by God the most high by the grace of the intercession of the prophet Mahomet, the envoy of God (may the peace and blessings of God be with him!). O my child, you must govern all your subjects with a spirit of justice, for in this world, until death, we ought to seek the truth. O my child, above all forget not my last instructions." Then, taking in her arms the royal child, she kissed him.

The Sultan Haroun-er-Raschid having told the Sultan of Roum that he wished to return to the country of Bagdad, the Sultan gave orders to his ministers to assemble the grandees, the officers, and the soldiers, with elephants, horses, and instruments of music. All came with presents, for the Sultan of Roum wished to accompany the Sultan Haroun-er-Raschid as far as Bagdad and carry him the presents. The favorable moment having arrived, the Sultan Haroun-er-Raschid departed from Roum, directing his way to the country of Bagdad, from plain to plain, and from halting-place to halting-place. After journeying some time, they rejoicing all the way, they arrived at the country of Bagdad.

The ministers, the chiefs, and the soldiers came out to meet the Sultan Haroun-er-Raschid, and they entered the palace. Then the Queen hastened to find the Sultan and her daughter, the princess Djouher-Manikam. Meeting her daughter, she pressed her in her arms and covered her with kisses. She said in tears: "Alas, my child! the fruit of my heart! I, your mother thought that she would never see you again." And she covered her body with tears and kisses, while she kept repeating, "Alas, my child! I thought you lost forever." Then the Queen bowed before the Sultan Haroun-er-Raschid. Her son, Minbah-Chahaz, then came to bow before his mother, but the latter pressed him in her arms and kissed him. Then her son-in-law, King Chah Djouhou, advanced and bowed before the Queen in his turn. And she pressed him in her arms and kissed him. All were in tears.

The Sultan Haroun-er-Raschid started for the hall of audience, and gave orders to one of his heralds to assemble his ministers, his warriors, and his subjects. When they were all gathered together the Sultan said: "Now I wish to entertain the ministers, the chiefs, and the officers who escorted us here." When the Sultan had finished entertaining them they desired to take leave and return to the country of Roum. The Sultan Haroun-er-Raschid made them gifts of vestments of honor, to each according to his rank. They prostrated themselves at his feet, and then returned in peace to the country of Roum.

Afterward, the Sultan Haroun-er-Raschid ordered one of his heralds to assemble his ministers, his officers, and his subjects. Once gathered together, the prince said: "O all of you, my ministers and my officers, you must build me a house of baths seven stories high, on the public square of Bagdad."

All responded, "O my lord, king of the world, whatever your commands may be, your servants place them above their heads." And all, ministers, officers, and subjects, gave themselves to the work, each of them doing what was directed by the architect. After some time, the palace of baths was finished. It was sumptuously adorned with curtains of silk, canopies, tapestries woven with gold and fringed with pearls. Rugs embroidered with gold were stretched on the different floors, and there was a quantity of torches and lanterns.

Then the builders came before the King and said: "O my lord, king of the world, your slaves have finished their work according to the commands of your Majesty."

The King Haroun-er-Raschid gave thanks unto God the most high, worthy of all praise, the true Lord who accords to his servants all their needs.

Then the festivals began. For forty days and forty nights the bands never stopped playing. There were sports, banquets, amusements of all sorts. They gave themselves noisily to pleasure, because the Sultan was going to proceed to the ceremony of the bath of the two spouses, his children. When the watches were finished and the favorable moment had come, the Sultan was arrayed in a magnificent garment embroidered with gold, while the princess Djouher-Manikam was adorned by her mother with superb veils and vestments trimmed with jewels, with pearls and precious stones of an incomparable richness. The spouses thus adorned, the Sultan made them mount a palanquin. His son, Minbah-Chahaz, was clad in a splendid costume.

The Sultan mounted his horse Sembaran, and his saddle was of carved gold. Surrounded by young princes and lords, by officers of his court and the standards, Haroun-er-Raschid marched at the head. He advanced, followed by princes, ministers, and officers. The wives of the grandees accompanied the Queen with her maids-of-honor, and all the musical instruments gave forth their harmonious sounds. Seven times they made the circuit of the city. When the two spouses had arrived at the foot of the Palace of Baths the Sultan made them ascend. Then came the spouses of the grandees with the Queen, who showered them with rice-powder mixed with amber and musk, and poured on their heads spikenard and *curcuma* (turmeric). They were both plunged into a bath of rose-water and extracts of all sorts of aromatic flowers, together with water from the sacred fountain of Zemzem.

The ceremonies of the bath finished, the two spouses went out of the Palace of Baths and went into the King's palace. On their arrival, they served a repast to the princes, the *orilemas*, the doctors of the law, the priests, the ministers, the officers, the common people, men and women. All without exception took part in the feast. When it was ended one of the doctors of the law recited the prayer asking God for perfect happiness, sheltered from all danger in this life and the next. Then he sprinkled showers of the most charming perfumes.

After that the Chah Djouhou went to find the Sultan, and said to him: " O my lord, king of the world, I have to ask your Majesty a favor and pardon. I wish to take leave of your Majesty and return to the country of Damas, for the country of Damas is forsaken, O my lord."

The Sultan said, " It is well, my lord. Your country, truly, is separated from its King. If it were not for your kingdom I would wish never to be separated from you, now that I have my daughter back again. But if I am inclined to commit a fault, do not comply with it."

Radja Chah Djouhou answered: " Your daughter is like a

soul which has entered my body. That is how I feel. But the countless favors of your Majesty to me, I place them above my head."

The Sultan Haroun-er-Raschid then said to his prime minister: "O my minister, get ready to start 3,000 soldiers and 300 horsemen. And have elephants or horses well equipped to transport my two children, husband and wife." When the escort was ready, then the Sultan commanded them to open the place where his treasures were stored, and forty-four camels were laden with riches, with vestments of woven gold and precious objects such as are found only in the palaces of kings.

All these preparations being finished, Radja Chah Djouhou took leave of his father-in-law, his mother-in-law, and his brother-in-law, Minbah-Chahaz. The latter all held in their arms and covered with kisses the princess Djouher-Manikam, as well as Radja Chah Djouhou. He and his brother-in-law Minbah-Chahaz wept as they embraced, and the people of the palace burst into sobs with a noise like that of the waves breaking on the seashore. Finally the princess Djouher and the King Chah Djouhou, after bowing before their father, mother, and brother, set out for the country of Damas, to the imposing sound of all the instruments of music. The Sultan Haroun-er-Raschid and his son, Minbah-Chahaz, conducted them outside of the fortifications. When they were far off, the Sultan went back to his palace, walking sadly with his son, Minbah-Chahaz, and praying God to bless his children.

After some time on the journey, the King Chah Djouhou arrived at the country of Damas. The officers and the soldiers sallied from the fortifications of Damas and went to meet the prince. The ministers and the officers bowed low at his feet, all rejoicing over the happy return and perfect health of the King and Queen. The prince entered his palace, and the two spouses lived full of tenderness for each other.

I will not prolong this story of the princess Djouher-Manikam, which has become celebrated in all countries to windward and to leeward. I close it here, giving my best wishes to those who shall read or hear it, and particularly to those who shall copy it!

MAKOTA RADJA-RADJA;

OR,

THE CROWN OF KINGS

—

[*Translated by Aristide Marre and C. C. Starkweather*]

MAKOTA RADJA-RADJA*

KINGS who are of the true faith, who have wisdom and follow justice, cause men worthy of their confidence to travel through their kingdom, to serve as their eyes and ears, and to make reports on the state and condition of their subjects, so that, knowing the cause, they may examine for themselves the conduct of the servants of God. But there are kings who do not rest contented with the report of their servants, and go themselves by night to see the condition and hear the complaints of subjects. Then they make by day a thorough examination of the matters thus come to their knowledge, in order to regulate them with justice and equity.

A story will illustrate this. Zeyd Ibries Selam tells what follows: The prince of the believers, the Caliph Omar (may God be satisfied with him!), judged the servants of God with equity during the day, and after pronouncing his judgments he went out of the city on the side toward the cemetery called Bakia-el-Gharkada. There he cut stone to gain money enough for the maintenance of his house, and when night had come he went through the city to know the good and evil of the servants of God. One night, says Zeyd Ibries Selam, "I accompanied the prince of the believers, Omar. When he was outside of Medina, he perceived a fire in an out-of-the-way place, and turned his steps thither. Scarcely had he arrived when he heard a woman with three children, and the latter were crying. The woman said: 'O God the most high, I beseech thee, make Omar suffer what I am suffering now. He sleeps satiated with food, while I and my children are starving.' The prince of the believers, Omar, hearing these

* Or, " The Crown of Kings."

words, went to the woman, and with a salutation said, ' May
I approach? '

" The woman answered, ' If it be by way of goodness, come.'

" He approached her and questioned her about her situation.

" The woman said: ' I come from a far place ; and as it was
dark when I arrived here, I could not enter the city. So I
stopped at this place. My children and I are suffering from
hunger and we cannot sleep.'

" The Caliph inquired, ' What is there in this kettle? '

" The woman answered: ' Nothing but water. I put it in
the kettle so that the children should imagine that I was cooking rice—perhaps, then, they would go to sleep and stop crying so loudly.'

" As soon as Omar had heard these words he returned
promptly to the city of Medina. Arriving at a shop where
they sold flour, be bought some and put it into a sack. In
another shop he bought some meat. Then lifting the sack to
his shoulders he carried it out of the city. I said to him:

" ' O prince of the believers, give me this sack, that I may
carry it for you.'

" ' If you bear the weight of this sack,' said his glorious
Majesty to me, ' who will bear the weight of my fault, and
who will clear me from the prayer of this woman in the affliction of her heart when she complained to the Lord of my negligence? '

" Omar, having said these words, continued to walk in tears
until he had come near the woman and her children. Then
he gave her the flour and the meat, and they ate till their hunger was appeased. The woman with a satisfied heart cried:

" ' May God the most high hear my prayer and render you
benefits, since you are so full of compassion for the servants
of God and are so much better than Omar.'

" The Caliph said to her, ' O woman, blame not Omar, for
he knew not how you fared.' "

There was once a king in the country of Syria named Malik-es-Saleh, very pious and just, and continually preoccupied with the state of his subjects. They say that every night
he went to the mosque, cemeteries, and other solitary places,
in search of strangers, fakirs, and poor people who had neither

home nor family. One night, arriving near a mosque, he heard the voice of a man inside the edifice. He entered and saw a fakir there. He could not see him distinctly, because he was covered with a mat. But he heard him, and this is what he said: " O Lord, if on the judgment-day thou shalt give a place in heaven to kings who are forgetful of the fakirs and the poor, then, O Lord, grant that I may not enter there."

Malik-es-Saleh, hearing these words, shed tears. He placed a piece of stuff before the fakir with 100 tahil of silver, and said to him:

" O fakir, I have learned from the glorious prophet (may peace be with him!) that fakirs become kings in heaven, after a life of self-sacrifice on earth. Since I am King in this perishable world, I come to you with the weakness of my nature and baseness of my being. I ask you to be at peace with me, and to show yourself compassionate to me when the moment of your glory in heaven shall have arrived."

When the Sultan Zayad sat upon the royal throne of Ikak, the country was infested with malefactors, brigands, robbers, assassins, and the like. The compounds were destroyed, the houses pillaged, and the people killed. The inhabitants could not sleep a single night in quiet, nor pass a single day in safety at home. A crowd of people came with their complaints to the Sultan Zayad, saying:

" The compounds are destroyed, the houses are pillaged, and the men are killed." All throughout Irak one heard nothing but reports of this kind.

One Friday the Sultan went to the mosque to pray. He then shut all the doors and said to the people in the mosque: " O servants of God now present in this mosque, know that a duty is imposed upon me. I must protect my subjects, for I shall have to give an account of my actions on the day of judgment. There are now in this country large numbers of malefactors, and many of my people have been ruined by them. It is my duty to repress these disorders. So, then, listen to what I have to say, and repeat it to those who are not present. I swear to you that all who shall, three days from now, leave his house after the hour of evening prayer, shall be put to death."

When the three days had passed and the fourth night arrived, Sultan Zayad mounted his horse and traversed the city with an escort of cavaliers. Outside of the city he came to a place and saw a man standing under a tree in the middle of a flock of sheep and goats. He said to him, " Who are you? "

The man said: " I come from a far-off village, and I am bringing sheep and goats to the city to sell them, and with their price to buy what I can for my wife and children. When arrived at this place I was so tired that I could not enter the city, and was obliged to stay here, with the intention of entering at daybreak and selling my sheep and goats."

Sultan Zayad, having heard this response, said: " Your words are true, but what can I do? If I do not put you to death to-morrow, when the news spreads, they will say Sultan Zayad is not faithful to his word. They will regard me with disdain, and no one will obey my orders. And the wicked ones will commit violent acts upon the good ones, and my country will be ruined. Heaven is better for you than this world." So he had him put to death and ordered that they should take his head.

During that same night all that he met were killed and beheaded. They say that in the course of that first day 500 persons were put to death. At dawn he had all these heads exposed on the highways, and published this proclamation:

" Whosoever shall not obey the commands of Sultan Zayad shall suffer the same fate."

When the people of the country saw these heads exposed at all sides on the earth, they were frightened, and a respectful fear of Sultan Zayad filled all hearts.

The second night Sultan Zayad went out again from the city, and that night 500 persons were killed.

The third night he remained out of the city till morning, but he did not meet a soul.

The following Friday Sultan Zayad went to the mosque, said his prayers, and declared: " O servants of God, let no one after to-day shut the door of his house nor his shop. I take upon myself the charge of replacing those of your goods which shall be destroyed or stolen."

They all obeyed his orders, for they feared him greatly. Their doors remained opened for several nights, and they never suffered the slightest loss. But after a while a man complained to the Sultan, saying, " Last night someone stole from me 400 tahil."

The Sultan said: " Can you swear to it?"

The man swore to the facts, and the Sultan had 400 tahil counted out to him in place of those he had lost. The following Friday, after prayers, forbidding anyone to leave the mosque, the Sultan said: " O servants of the Lord, know that 400 tahil have been stolen from the shop of a certain man. Unless you denounce the robber, not one of you shall escape, but to-day shall all of you be put to death."

Now, as he had rigorously commanded attendance at Friday's prayer service, the whole town had come to the mosque. They were seized with fright, for they knew that the Sultan kept his word, and they denounced the robber. The latter gave back the 400 tahil and received his punishment.

A long time afterward the Sultan Zayad asked, " At what place in my kingdom do they fear robbers most of all?"

" In the Valley of the Beni Ardou, in the country of Bassrah, for there they are numerous."

Sultan Zayad one day had the highways and paths of the valley strewn with gold and silver, precious stones, and stuffs of great price. All these things lay there a long time and not one was taken. Then the Sultan ordered them to take up these riches and give them to the fakirs and the poor. Then he rendered thanks unto God that he had thus securely established his law among his subjects.

Now it was in the times when Nouchirvau governed with justice and equity, protecting his subjects and causing his kingdom to prosper. One day he asked the grandees of his court, " Are there in my kingdom any places deserted and without inhabitants?"

The grandees who were there answered, " O king of the world, we know not in all your Majesty's realm a place which is not inhabited."

Nouchirvau kept silence, and for many days did not leave the palace. He summoned to his private chamber a learned doctor named Bouzor Djambour, and said to him:

" I desire to know with certainty if all parts of my realm are peopled, or if there is any which is not. How can I be sure of this?"

"To have your Majesty's desire fully satisfied you have only to abstain from leaving the palace."

Saying this, Bouzor Djambour took leave of the King and went to the audience-chamber of the King. He spoke to those assembled there as follows: "O ministers, generals, and all present, know that his Majesty is ill. Now, in order to cure him you must find for me a little bit of earth from a place in ruins and uninhabited. Those who are faithful servants of the King will not hesitate to accomplish immediately this act of devotion in his service, and to start at once in search of the remedy I have named."

These words were scarcely uttered when men were sent out to search the towns and villages and find some earth from a place in ruins and uninhabited. They found only one house in ruins, and the governor of the town said as follows about it: "A merchant once established in this dwelling. He died and left much wealth. As none of his heirs came forward, we closed the doors with stones and mortar, waiting for them to arrive. So the house has fallen to ruin."

Then the people took a little earth from beneath the house and took it to the King, telling him what had happened. Then the King called an assembly and said:

"Know all that my illness proceeded only from my fear that there might be in my kingdom a house in ruins. Now that it has been shown to me that there exists in my whole realm not a single place in ruins, but that the country is well populated, my malady is cured, seeing that my kingdom is in a perfect condition."

In the time of Nouchirvau a man sold his compound to another man. The buyer of this property, while engaged in making repairs, found in the earth many jars filled with gold which someone had buried there. He went immediately to the one who sold him the premises and told him the news. The seller said:

"That gold is not mine, for I did not put it in the ground. I sold you the compound; the discovery that you have made is yours."

The buyer replied: "I bought the premises alone: I did not buy gold; so it is yours." As each refused to take the treasure, they went to the King Nouchirvau and recounted the affair to him, saying, " This gold should be the property of the King." But King Nouchirvau would not take the gold. He asked the two men if they had children. They replied, " Yes, my lord, we have each a child, a boy and a girl."

" Well," said the King, " marry the girl to the boy, and give them the gold you found."

In ancient times a King of China fell ill and as a result of his malady he lost his hearing. He wept in sorrow over this affliction and grew very thin and pale. His ministers came one day and asked him to tell them in writing his condition. He answered: " I am not ill, but so weakened by my inquietude and distress that I can no longer hear the words of my subjects when they come to make their complaints. I know not how to act not to be guilty of negligence in the government of my kingdom."

The ministers then said: " If the ears of your Majesty do not hear, our ears shall replace those of the King, and we can carry to his Majesty the complaints and regrets of his subjects. Why, then, should his Majesty be so much disturbed over the weakening of his physical forces? "

The King of China answered: " At the day of judgment it is I, and not my ministers, who will have to render account of the affairs of my subjects. I must therefore myself examine into their complaints and troubles. I am sure that the burden of ruling would be lighter for me if I could have tranquillity of spirit. But my eyes can see, although my ears are deaf."

And he commanded them to publish this edict: " All who are victims of injustice must reduce their complaints to writing, and bring them to the King so that he may look into their troubles."

They tell also the following story: There was formerly in the city of Ispahan, a king whose power and glory had filled him with pride. He commanded his ministers to build him a palace in a certain place. The ministers, with the architects, ordered the slaves to level the ground so as to form a vast esplanade and cause to disappear all the houses of the neighborhood. Among these houses, they say, there was one belonging to an old woman who was very poor and without a family to help her. In spite of her great age, she went to work as well as she could, in different places, but could scarcely exist on her earnings. Her house near the site selected for the new palace was old and in a tumble-down condition. They tell that one day having gone a long distance to find work she fell ill and remained a long time without being able to return to her house. Then the architects who were building the palace said, "We must not let this hovel remain standing so near the King's palace." So they razed the hut and levelled the earth, and finished the palace with all sorts of embellishments. The King, taking possession, gave a grand housewarming festival.

Now on this very day it so happened that the old woman returned home. Arriving she could find no traces of her house, and was stupefied. In one hand she held a stick, in the other some dry wood for her fire. On her back she bore a package of rice and herbs for cooking. She was fatigued with a long journey and faint with hunger. When she saw that her house had disappeared she knew not what to do nor where to go. She burst into tears. The servants of the King drove her away, and as she went, she fell and spilled her rice and herbs and fell down in the mud. In this state of indescribable desolation she exclaimed, "O Lord, avenge me on these tyrants!"

The old woman had hardly ceased speaking when the voice of some unseen being was heard above her saying, "O woman, fly quickly from this spot, for the anger of God is advancing upon the King." In horror she got up and fled in all haste. Again she heard the voice saying, "O woman, look behind you at the palace." She looked behind her and saw the palace, the King, and all his ministers and servants engulfed in the bowels of the earth by the will of God. And to this day that place vomits fire and smoke as a mark and a warning.

In the Kitab Tarykh it is told that in ancient times under the kings of Persia named Moah, who followed the rules of justice, men were happy. But after these kings, Izdegherd-ibn-Chahryar reigned over Persia. By his harsh tyranny he destroyed the high reputation of the kings of Persia and wretchedly closed a series of reigns lasting 4,000 years and noted all over the world for justice and equity. Under the rule of this miserable tyrant countless numbers of men perished and a great many prosperous and famous cities were devastated. All the better classes of citizens were plunged into the most frightful distress and the most lamentable desolation, and it would be impossible to tell how great and wide-spread was the mourning. Now while all were groaning in affliction the King made merry.

One day in his presumptuous pride he assembled his ministers and his generals to show his royal power and his domination over the people. He was seated on his throne, surrounded by a crowd of courtiers, when suddenly a beautiful horse crossing the city at a gallop went straight into the palace of the King, among the ministers and the grandees. They all admired the beautiful horse, the like of which none had ever seen. Nobody dared to seize him as he pranced from right to left. Suddenly the horse approached the throne and laid down at the feet of the King. The King patted and stroked him, and the horse never moved. Then the wicked King began to laugh and said: "O my ministers, you see how far my greatness goes. It is only at my throne that this wonderful horse has stopped. I will mount and ride him on the esplanade." The King ordered a saddle brought, and was placing it on the horse with his own hands, when he received such a kick over the heart that he was immediately killed. Then the wonderful horse vanished, and no one saw where it went. The people all rejoiced and said, "Of a truth, this mysterious horse was one of the angels of God sent to exterminate a tyrant."

It was in the time of this King, and by his tyranny, that the kingdom of the sovereign of Persia was ruled and fell into the hands of another people. King Khochtacab, the most celebrated of all the kings of his time, by his power, greatness, and magnificence, had raised in rank a man named Rassat Rouchin, a name which in Persia signifies "sincere and brilliant." Influenced by this fine name, the King forgot all prudence, and without any proof of his capacity he raised this man to power and made him minister, turning over to him the care of the most important affairs in his kingdom and giving him all his confidence. His ostensible conduct was irreproachable, and his acts had for everybody the appearance of honesty and truth. One day the minister Rassat Rouchin said to the King: "The people, on account of our leniency and goodness, are forgetting their duty, and are showing no more deference nor respect. We must inspire them with fear, or affairs will not prosper."

The King in his blind confidence responded, " Do whatever you think is right." As soon as the minister had come from the palace of the King he addressed a proclamation to the towns and villages in which he said: " His Majesty is irritated with his subjects. You must all come with presents to appease his anger." From all sides arrived princes and ministers and grandees of the realm, with precious and magnificent objects. Seized with fear they sought counsel of the minister Rassat Rouchin.

" How," said they, " dare we present ourselves before his Majesty in his present state of anger against us? "

Then the minister responded: " If the instant of death is not yet come for you, I will try to save you. I tremble to admit you to the King. But what can I do? On account of the critical situation I will go alone before the King and present your case." So every day he conducted them only as far as the door of the King. There they were told of the fines to which they had been condemned. He took in this way what they had, and sent them home.

This sort of thing continued for a long while until the means of the people were exhausted and the treasury became absolutely empty. The King, always full of confidence in the uprightness of the minister, was in complete ignorance of all this. But at that time there was a king who was an enemy of King Khochtacab. When he learned that the subjects of the latter were suffering cruelly from the oppression of his minister and that his generals were weakened by hunger, he took heart and invaded the kingdom. Then King Khochtacab commanded that his treasury should be opened, and that they should take out all the wealth to gratify the army, gain the hearts of the generals, and defray the expenses of the war. But he found that there was nothing left in the treasury. The army, weakened, was incapable of resisting. The King, shut up in his fort, found it impossible to attack the enemy, and they ravaged and despoiled the kingdom.

The King, having been considered so great, was cruelly wounded by shame at his defeat. He knew not which way to turn his steps. His soul was profoundly troubled. One day, when he had gone forth from the city, wandering at random through plain and forest, he saw a shepherd's hut in the distance, at the door of which were two dogs hanging by the neck. Seeing the King, the shepherd approached and led him to his hovel and served him with the best food he could afford. But the King said:

" I shall not eat until you have told me why you have hanged these two dogs at your cabin-door."

The shepherd responded: " O king of the world, I hanged these two dogs because they betrayed my flock. As my flock was wasting away, I hid one day to see what took place. The wolf came and the dogs played with him and let him carry off sheep and goats. So I hanged the two dogs as faithless traitors."

The King returned to the city and thought over this singular story. " It is a lesson for me," he said, " a revelation. It is impossible not to see that my subjects are the flock and I am the shepherd, while my minister has acted like the shepherd's dogs, and the enemy who has my kingdom is the wolf. I must examine into the conduct of my minister and see with what fidelity he has served me."

When he had returned to the palace he called his secretaries and bade them bring the registers in which the accounts of the kingdom were kept. When these registers were opened he saw that they mentioned only the name of the minister Rassat Rouchin, and included such statements as: " Intercession of Rassat Rouchin in favor of princes so and so, ministers such and such, and grandees this and that, who ask pardon for their faults. Rassat Rouchin took their treasures and granted them grace." There was nothing else in the registers. When the King saw this he said:

" Who rests his faith upon a name goes often without bread,
While he who faithless proves for bread shall lose his soul instead."

These words the King had engraved in letters of gold and fastened to the gate. And at this gate he had the false minister hanged as the dogs were hanged at the cabin-door.

A King of Persia, in a fit of anger against his wife for a certain fault which she had committed, commanded his prime minister to put her to death, together with her nursing in-

fant. The minister, on account of the furious anger of the
King, did not dare to plead the Queen's cause, but took her
to his mother's house. The minister found another woman
who had been condemned to death and had her executed, telling the King that it was the Queen who was beheaded. The
King's child grew and flourished until he had become a handsome young man. But the King grew more and more morose
and melancholy, and shut himself up in the palace. The minister, noticing this continual sadness of the King, said:

"O king of the world, what has come over the heart of your
Majesty? Pray tell me the cause of your sorrow."

And the King said: "O minister, how should I not be sad
and disturbed? Here I am getting old and I have no son to
cause my name to live and protect my kingdom. That is the
cause of my sorrow and unhappiness."

When the minister heard these words he said, "O king of
the world, your sorrow shall not long endure, for you have a
son, capable of preserving and protecting your kingdom.
This son of yours has intelligence, education, natural gifts,
and great personal beauty, and is of most excellent character."

The King said, "Where is this son of whose existence I
have been unaware?"

The minister answered, "Your Majesty is not aware of his
existence, but I know that he is very much alive." The minister then related how he had spared the lives of the Queen
and her child. The King was transported with joy, and cried,
"Happy the king who has such a minister!"

The minister bowed low and said, "When shall your son,
the prince, present himself?"

The King answered: "Go seek forty young men of his
age, build, figure, and complexion. Have them all dressed
alike. Bring these forty young men with my son to a certain place in the plain. Await me there, but tell not this secret
to a soul. When I have arrived at the spot then cause these
forty young men to present themselves before me. If my son
is among them I shall most certainly recognize him."

The minister took leave of the King, and with a heart filled
with joy set about doing what the King had ordered. When
the King had arrived at the spot chosen his minister ad-

vanced, followed by forty-one youths, all dressed alike. As soon as the King had seen them he recognized his son and called him to his side. Then he went back to the city with him and all the grandees. The next day he invited the latter to a great festival, and gave to each of them a splendid present. He turned over his kingdom to his son, taking care to place him and his government under the tutelage of the good minister who had saved his wife and brought him up. Then the King went into a religious retreat, and as long as he lived occupied himself in the service of God.

The Sultan Alexander, called the Two-Horned, at the beginning of his reign sent an ambassador to King Darius, who was then at the zenith of his greatness. On his return, this ambassador made his report to King Alexander. The latter read it, but had doubts over a certain word therein contained. He questioned his ambassador about the word, saying, " Did you hear that exact word from the mouth of King Darius? "

The ambassador replied, " I heard it with my own ears."

King Alexander, not being able to believe it, wrote a second letter, mentioning this word, and despatched to King Darius another ambassador, charged to deliver it. When King Darius, reading the letter of King Alexander, came to this special word, he took a knife and cut it out, then wrote a letter to King Alexander, in which he said : " The sincerity of the soul of the King is the foundation of his realm and his greatness. His words, therefore, should be faithfully transmitted and reproduced by his ambassador. I have cut out of your letter a certain word, because it was never pronounced by me. And if your former ambassador were only here I would cut out his lying tongue even as I have cut out the word from your letter."

When this answer of King Darius's was borne to King Alexander he read it and summoned before him the faithless ambassador. " Why," said he, " were you willing, with a word, to cause the loss of many men and countries? "

" Because they showed me little deference and did not treat me well."

King Alexander said: " Foolish man ! And you thought that we sent you to look after your own personal interests, and neglect those of the nation? " He commanded that his tongue should be torn out, and made a proclamation, saying, "This is the fate of traitors who falsely report the words of kings."

In the Kitab Tarykh the following is recounted: The Sultan Homayoun sent an ambassador to the King of Khorassan. When this ambassador, on his arrival in the country, had delivered the letter of the Sultan to the King, the latter asked:

"How does your King conduct himself regarding his subjects? How does he govern them?"

"The rule of conduct and the mode of government used by my King," answered the ambassador, "are to make himself loved by all his subjects."

The King asked, "Of what nature is the affection of your King for his subjects?"

"That of a mother and father for their children and grandchildren."

"In hard and calamitous times, how does your King conduct himself?"

"He shows that he cares not for riches, for the door of his treasury is always open."

"In the daily receptions how does your King behave?"

"The receptions of my King resemble the gardens of Paradise refreshed by sweet breezes and scented with the balmy breath of sweetly smelling plants or like a sea filled with pearls and corals."

The King asked again, "And in council how speaks your King?"

The ambassador answered, "All those who hear my King in council become wise if they lack wisdom, and brave if they lack courage."

The King of Khorassan was enchanted with the answers of the ambassador, loaded him with presents, and said to him: "The spirit and judgment of your King are reflected in the person of his ambassador. They should all be like you." And he addressed in answer to the Sultan a letter filled with compliments and felicitations.

In the Kitab Tarykh it is related that the Sultan Mahmoud was fond of his servant Ayaz on account of the excellence of his wit and judgment. The other servants of the Sultan were jealous of Ayaz, and murmured against him. One day the

ministers and grandees were in the presence of the Sultan
Mahmoud, and Ayaz was standing respectfully before him.
Someone brought a cucumber as a present to the Sultan. The
Sultan sliced it and ate a morsel. He found it very bitter, but
gave no sign of this. He handed a piece of it to Ayaz, saying,
" Eat some of this cucumber and tell me how it tastes, so that
the others present may eat some of it also, and tell us if they
ever ate anything like it." Ayaz saluted, and ate of the cucumber with an appearance of pleasure.

" It is very good."

The King made the others eat of it. They found that it
was bitter, and were angry with Ayaz, and asked how he dare
to lie in such a manner.

" It is true," said the Sultan; " how could you say it was
good?"

Ayaz answered with respect: " May the Lord bless the
king of the world! How many favors have you given me!
How many sweet and savory dainties! How, then, could I
make a wry face over one bitter morsel? I ought, on the contrary, to declare that the bitterness of this mouthful is completely annulled by the delicious sweetness of the others, so
that your Majesty shall continue to bestow dainties upon me
as before."

A certain king, vain of his royal power, had a servant who
was very pious and a true believer, very punctilious in the
practice of his religious duties. The King distinguished him
above all the others as one in whom he could trust on account
of the integrity of his heart. He had given him this order:
" Go not far away from here, day or night. Keep close watch,
and neglect not my service." The servant, after finishing his
religious duties, took his post, where the King from time to
time sent for him. But the King had need of him, and he was
not to be found. They sent to look for him, but in vain, and
the King grew very angry with him. Finally the servant arrived and prostrated himself before the King. The latter, full
of wrath, demanded:

" Why are you late? Why don't you pay attention to my
orders?" And he commanded that the man be punished, to
make him more attentive to the King's service.

But the servant replied, " If I am late, it is only on account of the great embarrassment in which I find myself placed."

"What embarrassment? Tell me."

The servant, bowing low, spoke as follows: "My embarrassment comes from the fact that I have two masters to serve. The first is the true Master, he who created the universe and the children of Adam, whose punishments are very severe. The second is only the servant of the former, and not the true master. I am obliged to attend to the service of the true Master before the service of the second. That is the embarrassment in which I find myself."

When the King heard these words he shed abundant tears, and said: "From this day forth you are free. Follow the service of the Lord, and do not forget to pray for me."

The servants of the King should love their King more than they love their own life, their mother, their father, their children, their grandchildren, their family, their riches, and all that belongs to them. In a word, for them the person of their King should be above all, so that one may call them true servants of the King, and that in all truth they may be termed his favorites. They tell the story that one day the Sultan Mahmoud Ghazi (may grace be upon him!) was seated on his throne, surrounded by his ministers and his officers, among whom was Ayaz. The Sultan said to his treasurer:

"Go to the treasure-chamber. Take to a certain place gold, silver, precious stones, and other objects of great value. For we are going there to amuse ourselves, and present these treasures to those who shall accompany us."

One day the Sultan started to go and amuse himself at that place, and as soon as the news spread abroad, a great number of people followed him there. When he arrived he halted at a spot level, clean, and well lighted, and said to his treasurer:

"Expose my treasures here, in this place, so that all those who are happy shall obtain a present according to their degree of happiness, and that one may know who are those who have the most luck and those who have the least."

All hearing these words quickly approached, pressing forward, with their eyes wide open and their looks fixed on the treasurer, praying him to exhibit the presents at the designated place. At this very moment the Sultan spurred his horse to a gallop and rode from their presence. When he was far away and out of their sight, he stopped and looked behind him. There he saw Ayaz, the only one who had followed him. The others, preoccupied with getting their share of the treasures, never suspected that the Sultan had gone and was already far away from them. The Sultan, halting a moment, returned to the city.

On their side, the ministers and the grandees, having taken possession of the most precious objects, returned joyfully to their homes. On the way they compared notes with each other about their shares of the treasure. One said, " I had the best luck "; and another, " No, I had the best." And all, whoever they were, said the same thing, for all except Ayaz had their share of the King's presents. So they said among themselves, " It is clear that the one who has no luck is Ayaz."

Some jealous ones added: " In truth, Master Ayaz has no luck at all. By his lack of intelligence and good judgment he has had none of the Sultan's presents."

Ayaz heard all these remarks, but kept silence. Some days later, the Sultan came out of his palace and sat upon the throne. All the grandees came into his presence. Ayaz was standing before him. The Sultan asked:

" Who among you had no luck? "

The ministers answered: " It is Ayaz! He did not get a single one of your Majesty's many presents. It is clear that he has no luck, for he left all those precious objects and came back with empty hands."

The Sultan said: " O Ayaz, are our presents without value in your eyes, that you disdain them? I don't know why you took nothing that was within your grasp. You would have prevented them from saying that you have no luck. What was your motive in doing a thing that has the approbation of nobody? "

Ayaz responded: " May the days and prosperity of the King increase! May the presents never tarnish that he has given to his servants. As for me, I have more luck than those who received the presents of your Majesty."

The Sultan said, " O Ayaz, prove to me the truth of your words."

Ayaz responded: " If they found some part in the largesses which were given them, I found the author himself of those great gifts. If they found gold, I found the master of the gold. If others found silver, I found the master of silver. If others found precious stones, I found the master of precious stones. If others yet found some pearls, I found the ocean of pearls. Who, therefore, O king of the world, among all those who vaunt themselves as having luck, has more than I have?"

The Sultan replied: " O Ayaz, tell me what is the meaning of your words. Where is all that which you say you found?"

Ayaz responded: " May the most high protect the person of the king of the world, more precious to me than all those objects of price! In whatever place may be his august person, there I am, and I thus obtain all that my heart desires. When I am with your Majesty, and your Majesty is with me, what do I lack? Who, then, has more luck than I have?"

One day the Sultan Alexander was plunged in sadness, and kept himself shut up in his palace. The wise Aristotle came before him, and seeing him absorbed in sad thoughts, asked him:

" Why is the Sultan so sad and what keeps him from going out of his palace?"

The Sultan Alexander answered: " I am grieving at the thought of the smallness of this world, and of all the troubles I am giving myself and others for the sake of reigning over a world that is so little worth. It is the vanity of my works that renders me sad."

Aristotle replied: " The reflection of the Sultan is just, for what, in truth, is the world? Certainly it has not enough importance by itself that the Sultan should occupy himself with a vain kingdom. But the government of this world is a mark of the sublime and eternal kingdom of the other world, and this kingdom the Sultan can obtain by governing this present world with justice. Your Majesty must therefore give all his cares to the government of this world, to obtain finally in the other world a kingdom of which the greatness is beyond measure and the duration is eternal."

The Sultan Alexander heard with pleasure the words of his wise counsellor.

Two qualities are essential to kings, generosity and magnanimity. When a minister remarks, in his king, sentiments unworthy of his rank, he should warn him of the fact, and should turn him from unworthy actions. They tell that a king, having made a gift of 500 dirhems, his minister said to him: "I have heard from the mouth of wise men that it is not permitted to kings to make a present of less than 1,000 dirhems!"

One day Haroun-er-Raschid made a gift of 500 tahil. His minister, named Yahya, made by signs and by gestures every effort to prevent him from doing this. When all those who had been present were gone, Haroun-er-Raschid said:

"O Yahya! what were you trying to do with all your signs?"

The latter replied: "O prince of true believers! I was trying to say that kings should never let it be seen that they are capable of making presents of less than 1,000 dirhems."

One day King Mamoun-er-Raschid heard his minister, named Abbas, say to a servant, "Go to the bazaar and buy something with this half-tahil."

Mamoun-er-Raschid was angry with him and said: "You are capable of dividing a tahil in two! That is not proper in a minister; you are not worthy of the name," and he forthwith desposed him from office.

In the Kitab Sifat-el-Molouk it is related that the King Chabour, giving his last instructions to his son, said as follows: "O my son! whenever you make a present to anyone, do not bestow it with your own hands. Do not even examine or have brought into your own presence the gifts that you make. Whenever you give a present, see that it be at least the equivalent of the revenue of a town in value, so that it will enrich the recipients, and make them and their children and grandchildren free from adversity. Furthermore, my child, beware all your life of giving yourself up to operations of commerce in your kingdom. For this kind of affairs is unworthy a king who has greatness of character, prosperity, and birth."

King Harmuz received one day a letter from his minister in which he said: "Many merchants being in town with a great quantity of jewels, pearls, hyacinths, rubies, diamonds, and other precious stones, I bought all they had for your Majesty, paying 200,000 tahil. Immediately afterward there arrived some merchants from another country who wanted to buy these and offered me a profit of 200,000 tahil. If the King consents I will sell the jewels, and later buy others."

King Harmuz wrote to his minister the following response: "What are 200,000 tahil? What are 400,000 tahil, profit included? Is that worth talking about and making so much ado? If you are going into the operations of commerce who will look after the government? If you buy and sell, what will become of the merchants? It is evident that you would destroy thus our good renown, and that you are the enemy of the merchants of our kingdom, for your designs would ruin them. Your sentiments are unworthy a minister." And for this he removed him from office.

In the Kitab Sifat-el-Houkama it is said: " There is a great diversity of inclinations among men. Everyone has his own propensity. One is borne naturally toward riches, another toward patience and resignation, another toward study and good works. And in this world the humors of men are so varied that they all differ in nature. Among this infinite variety of dispositions of soul, that which best suits kings and ministers is greatness of character, for that quality is the ornament of royalty.

" One day the minister of the Sultan Haroun-er-Raschid was returning from the council of state to his house when he was approached by a beggar who said: ' O Yahya! misery brings me to you. I pray you give me something.'

" When Yahya had arrived at his house he made the beggar sit down at the door, and calling an attendant said to him: ' Every day give this man 1,000 dinars, and for his food give him his part in the provisions consumed in your house.'

" They say that for a month the beggar came every day and sat at Yahya's door, and received the sum of 1,000 dinars. When he had received them at the end of the month, 30,000 dinars, the beggar went away. When informed of his departure, Yahya said: ' By the Lord! if he had not gone away, and had come to my door for the rest of his life, I should have given him the same daily ration.' "

In the Kitab Tarykh the following is told: " There was

once upon a time a Persian king named Khrosrou, remarkable among all the kings of Persia for his power, his greatness of character, his goodness, and the purity of his morals. His wife, named Chirine, was of a rare beauty, and no one at that time could be compared to her, for she possessed all the virtues. Khrosrou passionately loved Chirine, and among the books, famous in the world, which speak of loving couples, there is one called ' Khrosrou and Chirine.' One day Khrosrou was seated in the palace with his wife Chirine, when a fisherman brought in a fine fish as a present to Khrosrou. The latter ordered them to give him a present of 4,000 dirhems.

" ' You are wrong,' said Chirine.

" ' And why?' asked the King.

" ' If, in the future, you made one of your servants a present of 4,000 dirhems he will not fail to say forthwith, " I am considered as the equal of a fisherman." If your present is less than 4,000 dirhems, then necessarily he will say, " I am considered as being less than a fisherman," and your actions will sadden his heart.'

" Khrosrou said: ' Your observation is just. But I have spoken, and I cannot reverse what I have said, for it is shameful for a king to fail in keeping his word.'

" Chirine replied, ' Never mind, I know a way, and no one can say that you broke your promise.'

" ' What is this way?' asked Khrosrou.

" Chirine answered: ' Put this question to the fisherman, " Is this a fresh-water or a salt-water fish?"

" ' If he answers, " It is a fresh-water fish," say, " I want a salt-water one," and the contrary. Then he will go away and you will be released from your foolish promise.'

" Khrosrou, who by love of Chirine could not help hearing her advice and following it, put the question to the fisherman. But the latter, suspecting a trap, said, ' It is both.' King Khrosrou began to laugh, and gave him 4,000 dirhems in addition.

" The fisherman, having received his 8,000 dirhems, put them in a sack and went away. On the journey, a dirhem fell to the ground, and the fisherman, lowering his sack, began to search for the dirhem that had fallen. When he found it, he placed it with the others and took up his march again.

Khrosrou and Chirine had both been witnesses of his action.
Chirine said to Khrosrou: ' Behold the baseness and the
lack of judgment of the fisherman. He wearied himself to
hunt for one dirhem when he had a sack full of them. Recall
him and do him shame.'

" Khrosrou, who from his love for Chirine was incapable
of resisting her words, and always obeyed them, recalled the
fisherman and said to him: ' Of a truth, you have a low soul,
and possess neither judgment nor dignity. What! One of
your 8,000 dirhems was lost and you deferred your journey
until you had found it? That shows the baseness of your soul
and your lack of judgment.'

" The fisherman made obeisance and answered: ' May the
prosperity of the king of the world increase! I sought not
the dirhem on account of its money value, but only on account
of the greatness and importance of the words engraved upon
the coin. On one of its sides is written the name of God most
high. On the other side is written the name of the King.
Had I not found the dirhem, and had left it on the ground,
then people passing would have trodden upon it, and the two
names inscribed upon it, and which ought to be glorified
by all men, would have been despised and disgraced, and I
would have been the accomplice of all the passers-by who
trod upon it. That is why I took the trouble to find the
dirhem.'

" Khrosrou was pleased with this answer and gave him still
another 4,000 dirhems. The fisherman, filled with joy, took
his 12,000 dirhems and returned to his home."

A man had committed a serious offence against King
Haroun-er-Raschid. Condemned to death, he succeeded in
escaping. But he had a brother. The King summoned the
latter and said to him: " Find your brother so that I may
kill him. If you do not find him I will kill you in his place."
This man not finding his brother, the King Haroun-er-
Raschid ordered one of his servants to bring him to be killed.
But this servant said: " O prince of believers! if the one who
received the command to put this man to death brings him
for that purpose and at the same time a messenger comes
from your Majesty with an order not to kill him, ought he
not to release him?"

King Haroun-er-Raschid answered, " He certainly ought to release him, on account of my orders."

" O prince of believers," answered the servant, " the Koran says, ' He who has a burden shall not bear another's.' "

Then the King said: " Set the man free, for this must cover his case, and means that the innocent should not perish for the guilty."

They tell that, a pundit appearing one day before the Sultan Ismail Samani, King of the country of Khorassan, the Sultan received him with great distinction, and at his departure saluted him most respectfully and escorted him to the door, taking seven steps behind him.

The next night he dreamed that the glorious prophet (with whom be peace!) spoke thus to him: " O Ismail, because you honored one of my pundits, I will pray God that after you seven of your children and grandchildren shall become great and glorious kings." They say that for many years the kingdom of Khorassan flourished under the paternal government of the successors of this Sultan.

The Sultan Abdallah Tlahir, as soon as he had taken possession of the throne of Khorassan, received the homage of a large number of his subjects. At the end of several days he asked, " Is there anyone of distinction in the country who has not come to present himself before me? " They told him, " There are two persons that have not come, one named Ahmed Arab, and the other named Mahomet Islam. But these two men never present themselves before kings and ministers."

The Sultan replied, " Since they will not come to find kings and ministers, I must go to them." So one day the Sultan repaired to the house of Ahmed Arab. The latter, immediately arising, remained standing a long time facing the Sultan. Then regarding him fixedly he said to him: " O Sultan, I had heard tell of your beauty, and I now see that they spoke the truth. Make not of that body the embers of hell." Saying this he returned to his prayers. The Sultan Abdallah Tlahir went away from the sheik's house weeping.

He then betook himself to the house of Mahomet Islam. At the news that the Sultan was coming to see him, the sheik shut the door of his house, saying: "I ought not to see him. I ought not to speak to him."

The Sultan departed in tears and said: "Friday, when the sheik goes to the mosque I will go to him."

When Friday came he was on horseback, surrounded by soldiers, awaiting the arrival of the sheik. As soon as he perceived him, he dismounted, approached him on foot, and saluted him. The sheik asked: "Who are you? What do you want of me?"

The Sultan answered: "It is I, Abdallah Tlahir. I have come to see the sheik."

The latter, turning away his face, said to the Sultan, "What connection is there between you and me?"

The Sultan fell at the feet of the sheik, in tears, in the middle of the highway, and, invoking God the most high, spoke as follows, "O Lord, forgive my faults, on account of the many virtues of this faithful sheik." And he was forgiven and became a good man.

The imam El-Chafei (may mercy be with him!), going from the city of Jerusalem to the country of Egypt, halted in a town called Ramla. One of the inhabitants of this town took him into his house and entertained him with many attentions. The companions of the imam El-Chafei perceived that he felt a certain inquietude, but none of them knew the reason for it. The more the master of the house showered his attentions and civilities, the more disturbed the imam seemed to be. Finally at the moment when the imam was mounting his horse to continue his journey, the master of the house arrived and put a writing into his hands. On reading this, the imam lost his worried air, and, giving orders to pay the man thirty dinars, he went on his way rejoicing. One of his companions asked him:

"Why were you so disturbed? What did the writing say? And why did you show so much joy in reading it?"

The imam El-Chafei answered: "When our host took us to his house I noticed that his face lacked the characteristic signs of honesty. But as he treated us so well I began to think perhaps I was mistaken in judging him. But when I read the writing he handed me I saw it was as follows: 'While the imam has been here I have spent on him ten dinars. He ought therefore to pay me back twenty.' So then I knew that I had made no error in reading his character, and was pleased at my skill."

The story is told that one day as the prophet Solomon was seated on his royal throne, surrounded by men, spirits, and birds, two women came before him, each claiming possession of a child. These two women kept saying, " It is my child," but neither could give proof. All their arguments amounting to nothing, the prophet Solomon commanded that the child should be cut in two, and that each woman should take half. When the executioner advanced, drawing his sword, one of the women bursting into sobs cried out in anguish: " O Prophet Solomon, don't kill the child. Give it to this woman, it is all I ask ! "

As the murder of the child never drew a tear nor a movement of anxiety from the other woman, Solomon commanded them to give it to the woman who had wept, because her tears proved her to be the true mother, and that the child belonged to her, and not to the other woman. Thus did King Solomon show his wisdom in judging character.

O you who are magnificent! listen, I pray you, and hear to what degree of sublimity generosity is lifted. In the Kitab Adab-is-Selathin it is said that two qualities were given by God in all their perfection to two men—justice to Sultan Nouchirvau, King of Persia, and generosity to a subject of an Arab sultan named Hatim-Thai. The author of that work says that in the time of Hatim-Thai there were three kings celebrated throughout the whole world, and rivals in showing the perfection of generosity—the King of Roum, the King of Syria, and the King of Yemen. But as none of them was as famous as Hatim-Thai, they became jealous of him and united in hostility toward him. They said: " We are the kings of vast countries, and shall we suffer a simple subject of an Arab sultan to be counted as more generous than we are? " And each of these kings thought to try Hatim-Thai and destroy him.

The first of the three who attempted the undertaking was the King of Roum. This King said to one of his ministers: "O minister, I hear tell that there is among the Arabs a man named Hatim-Thai, and that he is reputed the most generous

man in the world. I am displeased that my name is not as
noted for generosity as his. I want to make a proof and see
if his fame is true or false. I have heard that Hatim-Thai
possesses a horse which he loves as he does his own soul.
Well, we will ask him to give us this beloved horse."

The minister sent an envoy, with suitable presents and a
letter to give to Hatim-Thai. He arrived in a great storm of
wind and rain which permitted no one to attend to his affairs
abroad. It was already night, and Hatim-Thai had made no
preparations to receive a guest, but he received the stranger
with the marks of the highest respect and greatest cordiality.

" What need brings you here to-night? " he asked.

" Nothing but to visit you," replied the envoy, and he never
mentioned that evening his mission from the King of Roum.

As there was nothing in the house to eat, Hatim-Thai killed
his favorite horse and served it for his guest's supper. As soon
as it was day, the envoy presented the gifts and the letter from
the King of Roum. When he read the passage in the letter
where the King asked for the horse which had just been killed,
Hatim-Thai turned pale and could not say a word. The envoy, observing him in this state, imagined that he regretted
the gift of his horse, and said:

" O Hatim-Thai, if it is not with pleasure that you give your
horse to my master, think no more about it, and let me return
to my country."

Hatim-Thai answered: " O envoy of the King of Roum!
if I had a thousand horses like that one I should give them all
without a moment's hesitation. But last night I asked you
the motive which brought you hither, and you said it was
merely to visit me. So I killed the horse for your food, and
that is why I am afflicted with sorrow at my lack of foresight."
He sent the envoy back home with many other horses as a gift.

The envoy told the whole story and the King of Roum said:
" The renown of Hatim-Thai is deserved; he is the most generous of men." He made an alliance of friendship with him,
and the fame of Hatim-Thai grew apace.

The second one who tested Hatim-Thai's generosity was
the King of Syria. He said: " How can Hatim-Thai, who
lives in the woods and the plains, occupied in pasturing goats,
camels, and horses, be more generous than so great a King

as I? I will put him to the proof. I will ask rich presents
that he cannot give, and he will be shamed and humiliated
before kings and peoples."

So the King of Syria sent an envoy to Hatim-Thai to ask
for 100 red camels with long manes, black eyes, and very tall.
Camels of this sort are hard to find, only kings having four
or five. When the envoy had arrived he told Hatim-Thai
what the King of Syria asked of him. Hatim-Thai was full of
joy hearing the words of the envoy, and hastened to regale
him bountifully with food and drink. Then he searched among
his camels, but found none such as the King of Syria desired.
He ordered search to be made among the peoples of his nation,
Arabs and Bedouins, offering a large price. By the will of
God a Bedouin succeeded in finding 100, and Hatim-Thai
asked only the delay of one month in payment. The envoy
returned home with the red camels and many other presents.
Seeing them, the King of Syria was struck with astonishment
and cried: " Behold, we wished only to test Hatim-Thai, and
now he has gone into debt to satisfy our desire. Yes, truly
he is the most generous man in the world."

He commanded them to send back to Hatim-Thai the 100
red camels loaded with magnificent presents. As soon as they
arrived, Hatim-Thai summoned the owner and gave him the
camels with all their burden of riches, without keeping anything for himself. When the envoy, returning home again,
recounted all these things, the King of Syria marvelled and
exclaimed: " No one can equal Hatim-Thai. He is generosity itself, in all its perfection."

The third king, that is, the King of Yemen, was very generous, and wanted no one to rival him in this particular. So
when he heard of the fame of Hatim-Thai for generosity, he
was vexed and full of sorrow. He said: " How can that
poor Hatim equal in generosity a great king like me? I give
alms to the poor, I feed them, and every day I give them clothing. How is it possible that anyone can dare to mention the
name of Hatim-Thai in my presence as the most generous of
men?"

Now, at that time an ambassador of the King of Maghreb
arrived at the Court of the King of Yemen, who spoke of the
wonderful generosity of Hatim-Thai. He felt as if his heart

was burning, but did not let his grief appear, and said to himself:

" Everybody repeats the praises of Hatim, one after another, without knowing exactly who he is, of what birth, and what are the means which permit him thus to give hospitality. I shall cause him to perish."

The King of Yemen summoned a Bedouin, a bandit celebrated for his ferocity, without pity for the life of a man. The Bedouin arrived, and the King gave him gold, silver, and clothing. " O Bedouin," he said to him, " if you will perform an affair for us, we will give you whatever you ask."

The Bedouin answered: " O my lord, king of the world, what is your Majesty's will? "

The King of Yemen replied: " There is a man named Hatim-Thai, of the tribe of Thai, on the confines of Syria. Go to this country, and employ all the tricks you can to kill him. When you have killed him bring me his head. If you succeed in doing as I wish, whatever you ask, it shall be given you."

These words of the King filled with joy the Bedouin's heart. He said to himself: " Here is a good piece of work. For an old tattered cloak I will kill a man. Why then should I hesitate a moment for a superb cloak of scarlet? "

Taking leave of the King, the Bedouin set out promptly and went toward Syria in search of Hatim-Thai. After a while he arrived at a village near to Syria, and there he met a young man of a rare beauty. His face bore the marks of virtue, his language was full of sweetness and affability, his soul was righteous, and his heart compassionate. He asked the Bedouin where he was going. The latter answered, " I am from the country of Yemen, and am going to Syria."

The young man replied: " O my brother! I wish you would do me the favor to rest for a day and a night in my house, and I will do the best to entertain you. After that you shall go on your journey when you wish."

The Bedouin heard these words with pleasure, and went into the young man's house. There he was treated magnificently and regaled so lavishly that he thought he had never seen and eaten so much. He slept peacefully all night. At dawn he said farewell, eager to gain the end of his journey. The young man said to him: " O my brother, if it is possible, stay two or three days longer, I beg you, so that by my hospitality I may show all the sincere affection that my heart feels for you."

The Bedouin replied: "O my brother, truly would I remain some time longer here, had I not a most important and delicate mission to fulfil. It is impossible for me to stay and enjoy myself here, while I have not yet accomplished my errand."

The young man answered: "O my brother, what is this difficult and delicate affair which prevents you from staying here? If you will tell me, doubtless I shall find some means of coming to your aid, and lightening the burden which weighs so heavily upon your heart. But, now, what can I do since you tell me nothing?"

Hearing these words, the Bedouin kept silence. He said to himself: "This affair is not easy to execute. It might be of use for me to have a prudent and discreet companion to confer with him about it. Perhaps I should do well to talk of it to this young man and ask his advice."

And nevertheless he dared not yet trust his secret, and his perplexity was written on his countenance. He could not utter a single word, and remained very anxious.

The young man observing the state of the Bedouin said to him: "O servant of God, your embarrassment is evident; you fear to open your heart to me. God alone, in truth, knows the secrets of his servants. But, in your present situation, it may be that I can be of some benefit to you."

The Bedouin, hearing these words of the young man, said to him: "O my loyal friend, know then that I am an Arab-Bedouin of the country of Yemen; that of all the Bedouins of Arabia there is not one so wicked nor so great a thief as I, and that my fame as a bandit is celebrated throughout all Yemen. The King, having resolved upon a wicked deed, ordered his minister to find a man capable of performing it. As I had the reputation of being the greatest bandit of the country of Yemen, I was summoned to the presence of the King. As soon as his Majesty saw me he loaded me with presents and said: 'If you do as I wish I will give you many more presents of gold and silver and other magnificent things.' I replied, 'O my lord, king of the world, what is this affair?' 'You must go and kill a man named Hatim-Thai, who lives on the confines of Syria.' To this I replied: ' O my lord, king of the world, I am only a Bedouin, a poor robber, wandering in the forests and the plains. For drink I have but the brackish water of the marshes. For food I have only rats and locusts.' On account of my wretchedness, I obeyed the wishes of the King, and promised to execute this affair. But here I am, in a very embarrassing situation, for I do not know this Hatim-Thai, and I don't even know where his tribe is, the Ben-Thai."

The young man, hearing these words, began to laugh, and said: " O my brother, be not disturbed. I know this Hatim-Thai, and I will show him to you." These words rejoiced the Bedouin. The young man continued: " O my brother, know that the tribe of Ben-Thai inhabit this village, and that the man named Hatim-Thai is himself in this tribe. If you will follow exactly what I indicate to you, you will certainly accomplish your mission."

The Bedouin answered: " O my brother, I place my life in your hands. What must be done? "

The young man answered: " O my brother, there is a place where Hatim-Thai goes for recreation. It is an extremely deserted place, which no one ever visits. When he gets there he eats, drinks, and then he sleeps, his head covered with a cloth, and his horse tied near by. You will arrive at that moment, you will promptly execute the wish of the King, you will jump upon the horse and dash away from this place and go wherever you like."

The young man went then to show the place to the Bedouin, and giving him a poniard with two edges well sharpened, he said: " O my brother, to-morrow Hatim-Thai will come to this spot. Forget nothing that you have to do."

All the instruction of the young man were followed by the Bedouin. Early in the morning Hatim-Thai repaired to the designated place. He ate, he drank, and when he had finished his repast he tied his horse near by. Then, covering his head with a cloth, he fell fast asleep. At this very moment the wicked Bedouin arrived. By the will of God, just as he was about to assassinate the young man, a thought came into his heart. " Hatim-Thai is celebrated throughout the whole world for his generosity and his benevolence. Before I kill him, while he is still alive, I want to see his face." And he raised the cloth that covered his head. At the sight of the countenance of the sleeping young man he fell at his feet and covered them with kisses, saying: " O my friend! What have you done? You ought not to act thus!"

Hearing these words of the Bedouin, the young man said: " What could I do? For the one called Hatim-Thai is I. The head that the King of Yemen wants is mine. What other means could I employ?" He conducted the Bedouin to his house, regaled him again, and gave him all he needed.

Then the Bedouin took leave and returned to his country. As soon as he arrived in Yemen, he went before the King and recounted all the circumstances relative to Hatim-Thai.

Having heard the story the King shed tears, and said: " Of a truth, Hatim-Thai is liberal, benevolent, and noble, brave and generous." Afterward the King of Yemen made a friendship with Hatim-Thai that lasted as long as his life.

When the Sultan Yakoub invaded Khorassan and besieged the capital, the Sultan Mahomet, shut up in the city, made such a strong resistance that for a long time it was impossible to capture the place. But his ministers betrayed him by sending to Sultan Yakoub letters which showed how it might be taken. One only of these ministers, named Ibrahim Hadjib, abstained from sending any traitorous letters, and remained faithful to his master. After a while the city was taken and Sultan Yakoub ascended the throne. Then all the most important people of the country came to pay homage to him. The ministers who had betrayed the former Sultan were conspicuous in their demonstrations of joy. The Sultan Yakoub gave a pleasant reception to those who came, and made them suitable gifts.

After this he asked, " Who has not come to present himself before me on this day of rejoicing?"

The ministers immediately answered, " Ibrahim Hadjib is the only one who has not come to present his congratulations."

Then the Sultan asked, " Why has he not done so? Is he ill?"

" No," they answered, " he is not ill."

The Sultan summoned Ibrahim Hadjib, and the latter came into the royal presence. The Sultan, observing on his countenance evident marks of care and sorrow, spoke thus to him: "Ibrahim Hadjib, are you the minister in whom the Sultan Mahomet placed his confidence?" He replied in the affirmative.

"From what motive, Ibrahim Hadjib, did you keep silence, and send me no word of advice while the ministers of Sultan Mahomet, now here, sent many letters to show me how to capture the city? Why did you refrain from appearing before me at court to-day, at the same time with the ministers and grandees? Why, now that you are here, are you the only one to wear a sad and mournful appearance and a long face, while all the others show their joy? To all these questions you must truthfully respond. And if you speak not the truth you shall be put to death."

"If the Sultan wishes to hear the language of truth and will not be vexed by it, I will reply to each of his questions. To the first question, why I sent no letter betraying my King, I will say: Know, Sultan, that the Sultan Mahomet was the King of this country; that he gave me many presents and had full confidence in me, thinking that in the moment of danger I would be his companion and his counsellor. How could I, then, betray him? I knew you not, and had received no benefits from you. Would it have been just for me to send you letters and cause the fall of one who had been so bountiful to me?"

"Your words are just and true," said the Sultan Yakoub.

Ibrahim Hadjib continued: "As to the question why I abstained from presenting myself at court to-day, and why I wore so sorrowful a face, I answer: Know that I could not present myself before the Sultan, because he was the enemy of my master and benefactor, and brought about the ruin of my lord. That is why I wore a sad face in your presence. Beside, the children and grandchildren of my lord are plunged in grief and anxiety, and how could I be happy in your presence, like these hypocrites, who are very different elsewhere? I have told the truth."

When the Sultan Yakoub had heard these words of Ibrahim Hadjib, he cried: "God be praised! Up to this time I have heard tell of ministers, I have seen many kinds, but never have I seen nor heard of a minister like this one. Now, only for the first time have I seen a true minister and listened to the words of truth." The Sultan Yakoub loaded Ibrahim Hadjib with favors, made him prime minister, and gave him the name of father. As for the other ministers, he caused them to perish, with their whole families. Then he published this proclamation:

" Behold the fate of those who are faithless to their promises and commit treason toward their King, for they cannot be counted as men."

2532

THIS BOOK MAY BE